DEVELOPMENTS IN
HIGHWAY PAVEMENT ENGINEERING—2

DEVELOPMENTS IN HIGHWAY PAVEMENT ENGINEERING—2

Edited by

PETER S. PELL

Professor of Civil Engineering,
University of Nottingham, UK

APPLIED SCIENCE PUBLISHERS LTD
LONDON

APPLIED SCIENCE PUBLISHERS LTD
RIPPLE ROAD, BARKING, ESSEX, ENGLAND

British Library Cataloguing in Publication Data

Developments in highway pavement engineering.
Vol.2.
1. Pavements
I. Pell, P S
625.8   TE250

ISBN 0-85334-804-9

WITH 10 TABLES AND 57 ILLUSTRATIONS

Printed in Great Britain by Galliard (Printers) Ltd, Great Yarmouth

PREFACE

In the present and future climate of limited resources and escalating costs, highway engineers must be encouraged to obtain the economic benefits of better design, construction and maintenance of their road pavements. The aim of this book, and its companion volume, 'Developments in Highway Pavement Engineering—1', is to present some of the recent developments which have taken place in pavement engineering which are relevant to the objective of getting better value in road pavements for our money.

In books of this type it is not possible to give comprehensive coverage of all aspects of pavement engineering; the choice of topics is that of the editor and I have selected those areas in which, in my view, there have been significant developments. Each chapter deals with a particular topic and is written by an acknowledged expert in the subject. The authors contributing to both books in this series are representative of some of the many different interests involved in pavement engineering, namely, consulting, contracting, local authorities and materials suppliers, as well as research workers from government, industry and the universities.

The first book in the series dealt with the developments in analytical pavement design and related material characterisation, the design and compaction of asphalt mixes, cement stabilised materials and the skid resistance of road surfacings. This second book covers a further six important topics. Earthworks are an inescapable part of all road construction, and subgrade assessment an essential factor in pavement design—the latest developments in these topics are presented in Chapter 1. Aggregate is an important and widely used material for base and sub-base layers of pavement construction and developments in this field are covered in Chapter 2. Highway engineers consider that some of our roads are vulnerable to severe winter conditions. The problem of frost damage is discussed in Chapter 3 and it should be noted that improved methods of measuring the frost susceptibility of materials and more relevant design methods can have big economic implications.

With the current decrease in the amount of new road construction and the savage cuts in expenditure on roads generally, highway engineers are placing more emphasis on maintenance and strengthening of existing roads. The assessment of pavement performance and the design of strengthening overlays are dealt with in Chapter 4 and the vitally important aspect of proper management, planning and organisation of maintenance is discussed in Chapter 5.

Many United Kingdom engineers are now concerned with the design, construction and maintenance of roads overseas, where the conditions are such that UK practice is often quite inappropriate. Chapter 6 discusses these problems and presents the latest developments in pavement engineering in developing countries.

Although each chapter of this book deals with a specific topic, and is complete in itself, cross references are made to relevant subject matter in other chapters and in the first book of the series. Furthermore, each author has provided a very full list of references for the reader who wishes to study certain aspects of a topic in more detail. The new ideas and developments which have taken place in recent years, and which are presented in this book, should make it both interesting and informative for a wide range of readers. It should prove to be a useful reference work for practical civil and highway engineers as well as providing up to date information for students, lecturers and research workers.

A comment I wrote in the preface to the first book in this series is again appropriate, namely, throughout this book the treatment of many topics is based on fundamental principles and measurements which allow a more analytical and quantitative approach. This is as it should be, and the words of Lord Kelvin are, I think, very relevant. 'When you can measure that of which you speak, and express it in numbers, you know something about it.'

Finally, as editor, I would like to express my thanks to the individual authors for contributing their chapters and for so cheerfully and readily accepting the editor's comments.

P.S.P.

CONTENTS

LIST OF CONTRIBUTORS

BRIAN COX

Lincolnshire County Council, City Hall, Beaumont Fee, Lincoln LN1 1DN, UK.

J. W. FRY

E.C.C. Quarries Ltd, Rockbeare Hill Quarry, Rockbeare, Exeter EX5 2HB, UK.

P. A. GREEN

Scott Wilson Kirkpatrick & Partners, Scott House, Basingstoke, Hants RG21 2JG, UK.

D. W. HIGHT

Department of Civil Engineering, Imperial College of Science and Technology, South Kensington, London SW7, UK.

R. H. JONES

Department of Civil Engineering, The University of Nottingham, University Park, Nottingham NG7 2RD, UK.

C. K. KENNEDY

School of Engineering Science, Plymouth Polytechnic, Plymouth, UK.

Chapter 1

EARTHWORKS

D. W. HIGHT

Imperial College of Science and Technology, London, UK

and

P. A. GREEN

Scott Wilson Kirkpatrick & Partners, Basingstoke, UK

SUMMARY

A review is made of the developments which have taken place over the last two decades in those aspects of earthworks design and practice which affect pavement performance. The dramatic increase in size of earthmoving plant and hence of earthworks in highway construction has required an examination of earthworks stability, settlement and trafficability. Potential problems in these areas are being solved by improved methods of analysis, an increased range of construction techniques and materials, better appreciation of in situ soil behaviour, and the ability to monitor performance by field instrumentation. Better understanding of material behaviour has also led to the inclusion of hard and soft rocks, waste products and wet materials in embankment.

In conventional design methods, overall pavement thickness is sensitive to subgrade condition as measured by the California Bearing Ratio (CBR). New techniques for subgrade improvement are examined and methods which have been developed for predicting the equilibrium conditions under a completed pavement and for measuring CBR at these conditions are discussed.

1

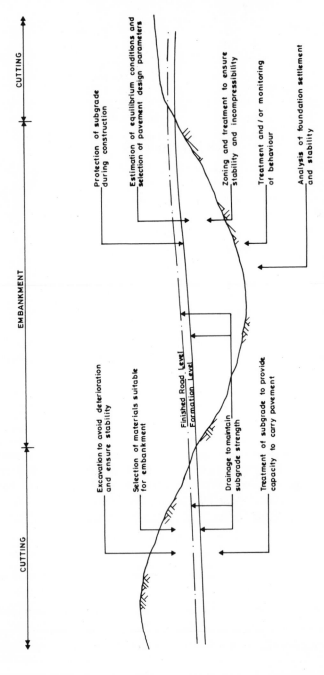

FIG. 1. Main aspects of earthworks design for roadworks.

INTRODUCTION

Construction of a road to the alignment, gradients and crossfalls selected by the highway engineer almost inevitably involves the adjustment of natural ground levels by a cut/fill operation. *In situ* soil or rock is removed to form cuttings and, if suitable, is placed in embankments. Where necessary, material from cuttings is augmented by soil or rock from borrow areas or by waste products. The materials forming the embankment and left in place in the cutting provide the foundation to the road.

In the zone immediately beneath the pavement (the traffic-stressed zone or subgrade) the materials must be capable of supporting the road pavement and its imposed traffic stresses without unacceptable deformation. The strength and stress–strain behaviour of these materials are obviously important parameters in determining the overall pavement thickness. These parameters can be controlled to some extent at the time of construction by selection and by treatment, e.g. compaction, stabilisation, etc. Protection of the materials in this zone by an impermeable pavement and by surface and sub-surface drainage is essential, however, if these parameters are to be maintained since they are usually dependent on moisture content.

Ground movements which would interrupt the drainage or impair the riding quality and safety of the pavement must clearly be avoided. Compression under gravity stresses within the bulk fill and its foundation should be avoided adjacent to structures and should be uniform and kept to a minimum elsewhere. The changed stress and drainage conditions in the embankment foundation and in the *in situ* ground around the cutting must not lead to their instability.

Several aspects of earthworks design can be seen to influence the performance of a road pavement and these are summarised in Fig. 1. Developments in the methods of analysis, construction methods, geotechnical processes, and materials which are relevant to these aspects of design are reviewed in this chapter. Some special earthworks problems which arise in certain overseas countries are mentioned in Chapter 6.

EARTHMOVING

The scale of the cut/fill operation that has been feasible has increased as a result of the dramatic developments in earthmoving machinery. Since the 1940s scrapers have increased in size from the 5 to 10 m^3 towed variety to the rubber-tyred motor scrapers of 20 and 30 m^3 capacity; these in turn have led to the current generation of 40 m^3 scrapers. Other items of plant, such as dump trucks, hydraulic excavators, draglines, tractor shovels, etc., have similarly increased in capacity. New methods of large-scale earthmoving for highway construction have also developed; in The Netherlands and Belgium hydraulic fills support road pavements, while in the UK Lewis and Parsons[1] describe the use of conveyor systems.

In the USA long hauls and dry summers have favoured the growth in size of earthmoving plant. In Europe, soil variability, limited haul lengths and wetter conditions have reduced the versatility of the largest US based scrapers and a limit to the size of machine used in earthworks in the UK appears to have been reached in the mid 1960s. Leflaive[2] considers that recent developments have been in terms of more efficient use of power and hence productivity, and increased flexibility and mobility in plant. He anticipates that continuous process machines which are used in open cast mines will be adapted and made sufficiently compact for use in highway construction.

There has been a parallel development in compaction plant to ensure a productivity compatible with the increased output of earthmoving plant. This has been achieved by increases in both roller width and in roller weight and by the introduction of high speed, self-propelled compactors. The range of roller types has also increased; towed static, sheepsfoot and grid rollers have been augmented by tamping foot and vibratory rollers. It is the improved effectiveness of the latter that has allowed increased layer thicknesses to be used and has helped in the satisfactory performance of rock fill in road embankments.

The growth in size of earthmoving equipment has introduced a dilemma for the engineer since it is frequently found that while material placed in the relatively low embankments involved in road construction will ensure their satisfactory performance, it may not be trafficable by the heaviest plant. Since he must produce the most economical design, the engineer has to consider whether he should upgrade his requirements for fills above those for satisfactory embankment behaviour to ensure that the plant most appropriate to the job can operate.

On trafficable soils, the stresses imposed by large earthmoving machinery may be sufficient to cause loss of soil strength. In the case of *in situ* soils this strength loss may be permanent as a result of remoulding. In the case of compacted soils the strength loss may either be temporary, being produced by positive pore-water pressures which subsequently dissipate or permanent if the trafficking stresses result in dilation and subsequent softening. To reduce the strength loss of subgrades, the Department of Transport Specification[3] requires protective layers to be provided, 150 mm on fills and 300 mm on cuttings. Croney[4] points out the special problem of trafficking damage at cut/fill transitions where protective overburden is often omitted.

CUT SLOPE STABILITY

Pavement performance may be affected directly by ground movements associated with deep-seated cut slope failures or indirectly by either the disruption of drainage as a result of instability or by the effects of drainage installed for slope stabilisation. Methods for assessing slope stability have been reviewed by Skempton and Hutchinson.[5] The only major development since that review, apart from the obvious increase in computer programs for analysis, has been the approach presented by Sarma.[6] In his method of stability analysis, Sarma determines the critical horizontal acceleration that is required to bring a mass of soil bounded by a slip line of any shape and the free surface to a state of limiting equilibrium; the critical acceleration is an indicator of the factor of safety. The method is suitable for hand calculations. Methods of slope stabilisation and their effectiveness have been examined by Hutchinson.[7]

In the context of cut slope stability, two important factors are now appreciated:

(a) The influence of pre-existing shear surfaces on stability. Failure along these surfaces may be reactivated by the removal of support in cuttings, Early and Skempton,[8] or by construction of embankments over them, Chandler et al.[9] The strength that is operational on such surfaces is the residual, Skempton.[10]

(b) The slow rate of equilibration of pore pressures in clay slopes from the initially low values following unloading by excavation to the steady seepage values, Vaughan and Walbancke.[11] This is probably the prime cause of delayed failure in stiff overconsolidated clays.

In the relatively shallow cuttings generally associated with road construction, instability does not necessarily result from increased shear stresses within the slope, but from the failure to relieve groundwater pressure, e.g. Cocksedge and Hight,[12] or to control groundwater flows which lead to seepage erosion. Unrelieved groundwater pressures and flows may cause deterioration of a cutting subgrade before the permanent drainage is installed and pre-construction drainage works or local dewatering may be required.

Developments in both plant and materials have enlarged the range of drainage measures which can be applied. Plastic pipes have replaced the traditional open-jointed earthenware or concrete pipes; they are light and can be laid in long lengths without jointing, making them suitable for use with rapid methods of mechanical excavation, e.g. Ground Water Services 'Drainflex' system. Mobile shoring systems, e.g. 'Ramshor', now permit safe and fast drain installation through unstable ground prior to cutting. Techniques for dewatering are summarised by Cashman and Haws.[13]

EMBANKMENTS

The numerous motorways, expressways and other high speed roads constructed during the last 20 to 30 years have required high standards of alignment, and this in turn has forced highway engineers to build roads on embankments. In such cases a number of considerations have to be taken into account to ensure adequate performance of the pavement. These include investigation of the embankments foundation, particularly if there is soft ground; the specification, selection, compaction and performance of the embankment fill; and problems associated with using difficult fill materials.

Foundations

Embankments on soft ground—conditions which the engineer would have previously avoided—usually cause the most difficulties. In such cases there are a number of factors for the engineer to consider. Firstly, he must ensure that the embankment will be stable, and new procedures for this have been developed. For example Symons[14] has reviewed the limitations and range of application of both the total and effective stress approaches to the problem and has provided stability charts based on the effective stress method linked with field measurement of pore-water pressures. Secondly, the engineer must check that the long term differential settlement of the pavement due to consolidation of the embankment foundations will not be such as to cause an unacceptably irregular riding surface or a significantly reduced pavement life. Thirdly, he must ensure that the total settlement of pavement will not exceed a certain predetermined limit, both as a means of limiting differential settlement and to avoid problems with drainage. The drainage problem is frequently an important consideration because embankments on poor foundations often occur in flat terrain which is subject to periodic flooding.

Fortunately, the safe construction of road embankments on soft foundations can now be carried out with confidence because of developments over the last 20 years. These developments include both improvements in design methods and the introduction of new construction techniques.

Improvements in design methods have resulted from a better appreciation of soil behaviour and recognition of the importance of *in situ* soil structure; improved methods of analysis; and, perhaps most important of all, advances in field instrumentation. The large number of recent, quantitative field studies, often at full scale (Bishop and Green[15]), has enabled engineers to compare actual performance with calculated performance based on sampling and laboratory testing. Discrepancies which do occur can often be explained by inappropriate design methods and/or disregard for the actual soil structure existing in the field; examples of this have been published by Rowe.[16,17] Improved methods of analysis have arisen from the development of computers to handle large amounts of data which has led in turn to the use of numerical methods based on finite elements and finite differences. Using these methods it is often possible to predict with reasonable accuracy the displacements under an embankment and the long term consolidation settlement in heterogeneous soils, as illustrated in studies by Wroth and Simpson[18] and Murray.[19,20] Few of these advances would have been possible without the development of instruments such as piezometers, pressure cells and extensometers. In view of these developments the British Geotechnical Society held a conference on field instrumentation in 1973 and the proceedings of that conference[21] forms a comprehensive review of the subject.

Improvements in instrumentation have not only helped to improve design methods and the correct choice of design parameters, but they have also assisted in the development of new construction techniques to treat soft or loose ground under embankments. Firstly, these instruments have facilitated the use of surcharging and/or preloading as a treatment for embankments on compressible soils; this is illustrated by the example in Figs. 2(a) and (b) from the M62 Motorway, Yorkshire. Secondly, field studies in the use of new techniques such as rock columns, McKenna *et al.*,[22] vibroflotation to densify loose sands, sand drains or cardboard wicks to accelerate consolidation, De Beer *et al.*,[23] and dynamic compaction, Menard and Broise[24] to stabilise bad ground under embankments have

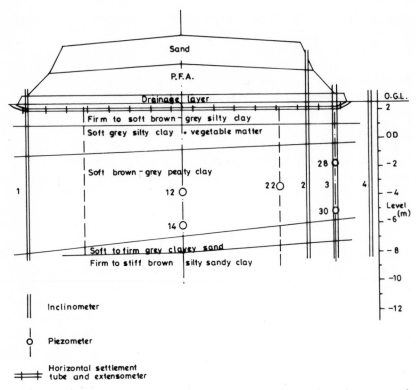

FIG. 2(a).   M62 Motorway, Yorkshire. Cross-section through an instrumented embankment over soft ground.

shown how and when to use these techniques to best advantage. A situation has now been reached in which the highway engineer has a number of procedures at his disposal to deal with difficult embankment foundation conditions. If none of these are applicable, he can at least monitor what is happening within the foundation soils, thereby enabling him to predict future behaviour.

Bulk Fill Materials

The requirements of stability and limited total and differential settlement at pavement level are met not only by design and treatment of the embankment foundations but by selection of the material used as bulk fill and by its treatment (excavation, processing, placing, compaction and drainage). Bulk fill material must, therefore, be relatively incompressible

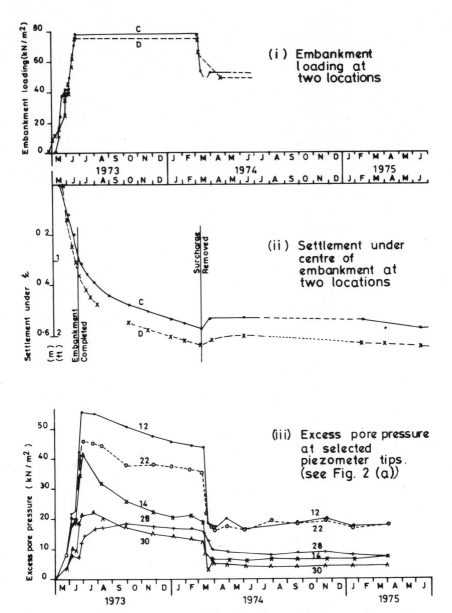

FIG. 2(b). M62 Motorway, Yorkshire. Loading, settlements and pore-water pressures for an embankment over soft ground.

and have sufficient strength to prevent general shear failure within the bank during and after its construction. In addition, the material must be capable of supporting the construction traffic required for its economic placement and treatment.

Compaction is an essential treatment for material placed in embankment since increasing a fill material's density by excluding air increases its strength and reduces both its compressibility and the deterioration which occurs on increase in moisture content. Until 1969 road embankments in Britain were compacted to the requirements of an 'end-product' specification based on the percentage air voids in the compacted material. However, with the increasing size of earthworks, checks on the air content using the sand replacement method became too laborious and a 'method' specification was introduced (see Table 6/2 of Clause 608 of the Department of Transport Specification[3]) which was based on research by the Transport and Road Research Laboratory (TRRL) on the performance of field compaction equipment. In this specification, requirements in terms of maximum depth of compacted layer and minimum number of passes of each type of compaction plant are described for three soil groups. While the method specification limits layer thickness in an attempt to avoid density gradients, it perhaps pays insufficient attention to the influence of water content on the depth of the compaction effect—Leflaive[2] comments on this aspect.

Soils

The criteria for selection and treatment of bulk fill materials logically depends on the position of the material within the embankment, the height of the embankment, and on the changes which take place in the material properties during construction and after completion of the pavement. However, it is not usually feasible to construct zoned road embankments with different criteria for selection and treatment in each zone; instead blanket criteria for suitability are established. Snedker[25] has examined the requirements for trafficability, stability and incompressibility of both granular and cohesive soils and provides guidance on selecting an upper limit of moisture content for use in the Department of Transport Specification.[3] He points out how the moisture content limit is usually close enough to optimum moisture content to ensure compactibility.

Examining first the question of trafficability of soils, Farrar and Darley[26] have produced useful data for establishing the soil conditions required for economic operation of various items of earthmoving plant on wet cohesive soils. By studying the performance of a number of towed and rubber-tyred scrapers on a range of soils they were able to relate the depth of rut produced by a scraper and its ease of movement to moisture content and shear strength of the fill. Their findings are reproduced in Table 1.

In this work and in earlier work on the subject of trafficability, e.g. Rodin,[27] the suitability of fill has been related either directly or indirectly via moisture content to its shear strength. It has been implicitly assumed

TABLE 1

LIMITING CONDITION OF COHESIVE FILL FOR OPERATION OF SCRAPERS WITHIN SPECIFIED LIMITS OF EFFICIENCY (AFTER FARRAR AND DARLEY[26])

	Maximum ratio of moisture content to plastic limit		Minimum vane shear strength $(kN m^{-2})$
	50% or more of silt and clay	Less than 50% of silt and clay	
Towed and small scrapers (less than 15 m³):			
Most efficient operation	1·1	0·9	140
Feasible operation	1·3	1·2	60
Medium and large motorised scrapers (over 15 m³):			
Most efficient operation	1·0	0·9	170
Feasible operation	1·2	1·1	100

Most efficient operation = minimum maintenance of haul road and formation with 50 mm deep ruts.
Feasible operation = haul road and formation maintenance is possible but with rutting up to 200 mm deep.

that deformations under construction traffic are acceptably small. There are, however, a group of compacted soils which, despite high undrained shear strengths, undergo large, apparently recoverable, deformations when subjected to rolling wheel loads. Such deformations prevent the proper compaction of overlying layers and, in the case of bound pavement layers, can result in damage. Experience of these problems with glacial tills has been presented by Cocksedge and Hight[28] who describe how the Benkleman Beam was used to quantify the problem and its solution.

Trafficability is inevitably closely related to the weather and effects of wetting and drying. Improved short term weather forecasts are now available for construction sites but the problems of organising operations, discussed by Norman,[29] remain.

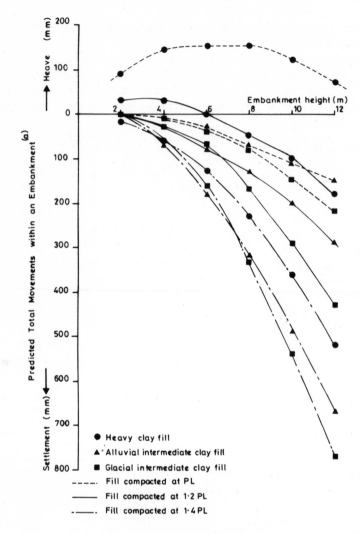

FIG. 3.   Predicted-total vertical movements within an embankment for a range of
embankment heights and for three soil types compacted at three different moisture
contents (based on Farrar[30]).

Settlement and stability within the embankment are both related to embankment height and placement moisture content. Stability is only likely to be critical in high embankments built with sandy clays and wet plastic clays; in these cases excess pore pressures may be developed and stability is at a minimum at the end of construction. Farrar[30] suggests that the use of Taylor's charts is sufficient for selecting the side slopes required for end of construction stability.

Estimates of the consolidation settlement of compacted clay embankments after completion of the pavement can be made by referring to Fig. 3 which is based on tabulated information presented by Farrar.[30] Settlements have been related to height of embankment and the ratio moisture content to plastic limit for three soils. For the heavy clay it was assumed that no settlement would take place during construction, whereas for the alluvial and glacial clays allowances have been made for settlements during an assumed 1 year construction period.

It can be seen from this review that conventionally the behaviour of soil, and hence its suitability as bulk fill, is related to moisture content and a parameter to take account of variability in soil type, viz. plastic limit for cohesive soils or optimum moisture content for granular soils. Snedker[25] questions the use of plastic limit in view of potential operator error and Dennehy[31] presents data which indicates the danger of using this parameter. Figure 4, taken from Dennehy, demonstrates that although the relationship between shear strength and moisture content is of the same form for different clays at low air voids, the ratio of moisture content to plastic limit at a given shear strength varies with soil type. Dennehy suggests that the ratio moisture content to liquid limit provides a more reliable means of ensuring that material of the required shear strength is accepted.

Criteria based on moisture content, whether related to plastic or liquid limit, have a major drawback in operation because of the delay in obtaining moisture content measurements. (Despite the proliferation of methods proposed for the rapid measurement of moisture content, none has yet been shown to be reliable, refer OECD,[32] although the approach proposed by Parsons[33] appears to be promising.) A criterion based on undrained shear strength, C_u, measured for example by vane or in unconfined tests, overcomes this drawback and the measurement automatically includes the effect of variation in soil type. It has the additional advantage that when stability is critical, shear strength is the relevant design parameter. However, correlation of C_u with compressibility must first be established if settlement is the governing factor. Vaughan et al.[34] describe the use of shear strength as a criterion for suitability of boulder clay for an embankment

		L.L.%	P.L.%	P.I.%	ACTIVITY $\frac{P I}{CLAY}$	SOIL AT 40 kN/m² M.C.%	$\frac{M.C.}{P.L.}$	L I
A	Reading Beds	70	22	48	0·91	20·5	0·93	–0·03
B	Bagshot Beds	56	20	36	1·16	26·0	1·30	0·17
C	Weathered London Clay	62	22	40	1·18	27·8	1·26	0·15
D	Unweathered London Clay(LL>70)	78	26	52	1·13	33·5	1·29	0·14
E	Unweathered London Clay(LL<50)	47	20	27	1·18	23·0	1·15	0·11

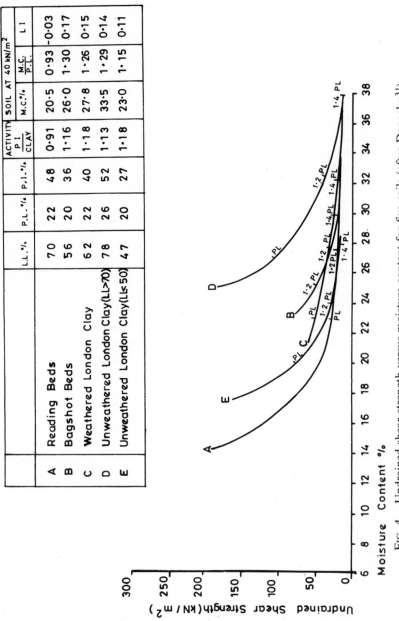

FIG. 4. Undrained shear strength versus moisture content for five soils (after Dennehy[31]).

dam, while Kent County Council has based the suitability of Gault Clay for bulk fill on its shear strength, measured in a vane test, rejecting soil with a strength less than $50 \, \text{kN m}^{-2}$.

Rock Fill

Road embankments constructed wholly with excavated hard rock are not common; where available from cutting, rock fill is generally used, either in de-bog operations or as a capping layer to the fill. On the grounds of trafficability and stability, rock fill is, however, eminently suitable for use in road embankments but, in the past, it has presented problems due to post-construction settlements. Penman[35] has explained how our understanding of rock fill behaviour has improved over the last decade and now marginal weak and friable rocks can be confidently used in major embankments. It has become apparent that to minimise rock fill settlement, intergranular forces should be kept low by grading so that there is a minimum of voids and a maximum of particle contacts, and particles should be prevented from moving into a denser packing by compaction.

Following this approach, and taking advantage of the increased size and power of compacting machinery, compacted rock fill embankments have been successfully constructed, the prime example of one carrying a road being Scammonden Dam, Mitchell and Maguire.[36]

The road-building programme of the last two decades has involved construction in a number of soft rocks and techniques for their excavation, handling, placing and compaction have been developed; these have enabled them to be regarded as suitable for bulk fill. Not surprisingly construction in Chalk, which represents in exposed area 15 % of the major geological formations in England, has received the most attention, but experience gained in its use is applicable to other soft rocks.

In their intact state these materials are capable of sustaining the gravity stresses imposed in most highway embankments. However, the open-textured soft rocks derive their strength from cementation and when this is destroyed, either in excavation or by compaction and trafficking, water is released causing temporary instability in the upper layers of compacted fill. Parsons[37] describes this problem in Chalk, the natural moisture content of which was close to the liquid limit of the remoulded material.

To meet the criteria for use in embankments, specifications for Chalk construction have concentrated on maintaining the lump structure of the Chalk by requiring vertical face excavation, the use of rippers to increase the depth of cut, the use of lightweight plant, and the prohibiting of subgrade trafficking. The degree of weathering of *in situ* Chalk varies, so,

TABLE 2

QUANTITIES OF MAJOR WASTE MATERIALS AVAILABLE (AFTER SHERWOOD[42])

Material	Distribution	Total quantity available (million tonnes)	Annual production (million tonnes)	Current annual use for all purposes (million tonnes)
Colliery shale	Chiefly in Midlands, North, S. Wales and Central Scotland	3 000	50	8
Pulverised fuel ash	Country-wide	—	7·5	⎱
Furnace bottom ash	Country-wide	—	2·5	⎰ 6
China clay waste: waste sand	Devon and Cornwall	125	10	⎱
other wastes		155	12	⎰ 1
Slate waste	N. Wales, Lake District and Cornwall	300–500	1·2	0·03
Incinerator waste	Country-wide (47 plants)[a]	[b]	0·6 (1·9[a])	[b]
Hassock	Kent		[b]	[b]
Spent oil shale	Scotland	330	None	

[a] Projected amounts by 1980.
[b] No information available.

therefore, does its behaviour as a bulk fill material and so do the measures required for its successful use. Ingoldby and Parsons[38] suggest that the onset of unstable conditions in Chalk is related to its moisture content and the percentage of fines and they have proposed a classification for predicting Chalk behaviour based on its saturation moisture content, its resistance to crushing and the method used in its handling.

Ingoldby and Parsons[38] have demonstrated that the choice of excavation plant has a greater influence on the degree of crushing than the compaction specification. Furthermore, since settlements of lightly compacted Chalk fills have occurred after soaking, Parsons recommends that Chalk is compacted according to the Department of Transport Specification[3] and that the classification to maintain stable conditions assumes this level of compaction.

In the USA, problems of excessive settlement and slope failure have been reported by Shamburger et al.[39] for road embankments constructed with 'shales' (which include weak sedimentary rocks such as claystones, siltstones and mudstones) placed in 1 m lifts with compaction by the hauling and spreading equipment. Physical and chemical weathering of the shale into clay or silt after construction have been identified as the primary causes of trouble. UK experience, Kennard et al.,[40] has demonstrated that if well broken up when excavated, placed in relatively thin layers and heavily compacted, near surface shales form suitable bulk fill. Vaughan[41] reports an investigation into the risk of deterioration in strength of a comparatively weakly cemented shale, which concluded that mechanical grinding could reduce the strength to that of the parent clay, but that this reduction could not be achieved by the placing plant. Vaughan regarded the clay strength as a useful lower bound to the strength of the fill.

Waste Products

A number of waste products meet the criteria for incorporation in road embankments if regarded as soils and they are being used increasingly, so taking advantage of their considerable environmental benefits of avoiding borrow areas and conserving useful materials. The TRRL has recently reviewed the properties of some of these products and gives examples of their application, Sherwood,[42–44] and Roe.[45] Table 2 summarises the quantities of major waste materials available and is taken from Sherwood.[42]

Pulverised fuel ash (PFA) has been used as a fill material since the 1950s and its engineering behaviour has been discussed by Sutherland et al.[46] In use, the material presents some difficulties as a result of its variation in moisture content, grading and specific gravity which make control testing difficult and require flexibility in its handling and treatment—PFA is also frost-susceptible (see Chapter 3). Two of its characteristics however, are particularly useful in road embankments. Firstly, it has self-cementing properties when compacted, which, although variable, limit the settlement that occurs within it, making it suitable for use at bridge abutments. Secondly, it has a low dry density making it ideal for lightweight fills on soils of low bearing capacity, e.g. at M62, Fig. 2(a). For compaction, PFA is classed as uniformly-graded.

Burnt and unburnt colliery shales, which originate either as waste from mines or from separation plant, are now being used extensively as a fill material. Information on the engineering properties of this material is given by McKechnie Thomson and Rodin[47] and Kennard et al.[40] These shales contain leachable sulphates which, together with their frost susceptibility, are a constraint on their use. Recommendations on permissible sulphate levels have been given by Sherwood and Ryley.[48] A limit must also be set on the percentage of combustible material which is included and a cladding of inert material is often specified as a precaution against spontaneous combustion. However, the state of compaction achieved in these shales is such that the air content is too low to allow combustion to take place. Colliery shales are classified as well-graded granular and dry cohesive soils.

Roe[45] discusses the use of incinerated refuse as a bulk fill, suggesting that it could be classified as either a well-graded granular or dry cohesive soil. He describes its use in a trial road at Edmonton.

Wet Fills

It is not always possible or economic for the highway engineer to select for use in road embankments only those materials which comply with a particular specification. In wet climates it may not be possible to dry out material, and the removal of such material, including its replacement by suitable imported fill, may be very costly. In such circumstances the use of wet fill can result in the minimum earthworks cost, as illustrated by Lindsay[49] for the M6 Motorway in northwest England.

Rodin[50] has suggested that material wetter than that normally allowed by current specifications can be used to build stable embankments provided the design of the embankment is carefully reviewed or special measures, such as drainage layers to accelerate consolidation, are introduced into the embankment. He suggests that a more realistic and economic limit for the placement of fill may be that at which it is practicable to place and compact the material. However, as the current specification limits of moisture

content are closely linked to compaction requirements it seems unlikely
that adequate compaction of wet fill material can be obtained by
equipment. In such circumstances accelerated consolidation is the only
means of producing a stable, non-settling embankment in a reasonable time
scale.

In addition to field studies (McLaren[51]), and experience on the M6
Motorway, recent laboratory studies by Huang and Shepard[52] in the USA
and by Farrar[30] in Britain have shown that some wet materials can be used
for road embankments provided proper drainage is provided. However,
Farrar has pointed out that the use of these materials will reduce the
efficiency of earthmoving thereby increasing the unit cost for handling the
material. This extra cost, together with the cost of drainage layers, etc.,
must be off-set by an equal or greater saving achieved by reducing or
eliminating the amount of imported material.

Reinforced Earth

Earth fill cannot be relied on to stand permanently at a slope of more than
about 35°, but if adequately reinforced with, bars, fibres, nets or steel strips
in horizontal layers, it will stand with a vertical face provided the soil at the
face is contained and protected from erosion. Vidal[53] has described this
technique of reinforced earth.

The technique is now used commonly on the Continent in highway
embankments, particular on steep sidelong ground and over areas of poor
foundation where the flexibility of reinforced earth can cater for large
differential settlements. The method of construction, which requires no
heavy equipment other than that for earthmoving, is particularly attractive
for highway interchanges since land requirements and fill volumes can be
substantially reduced. Since reinforced earth has a high resistance to
vibration it is entirely suitable as a pavement support.

NEW MATERIALS ✓

Synthetic fibre fabrics have been introduced into civil engineering within
the last ten years and already their use in geotechnical engineering has been
the subject of an international conference.[54] While the exact properties of
these fabrics can be varied in manufacture, they are intrinsically permeable,
flexible and of high tensile strength. These properties combine to render
them suitable for application in earthworks as membranes which can
provide separation, filtration and/or reinforcement.

The value of fabrics in supporting construction traffic on temporary haul roads on poor foundations is well proven, McGown and Ozelton.[55] Placed at the interface between the subsoil and the granular fill, a fabric will assist in achieving separation of the two materials while allowing both to drain; this means that the overlying fill retains its shear strength and pumping type failures are avoided. When deformations beneath wheel loads become large the fabric's tensile strength contributes an additional reinforcing effect. A proven rationale for selecting the appropriate granular layer thickness to use in conjunction with a permeable membrane on a soft foundation is urgently needed, since failures are relatively expensive to remedy. Trials for haul road construction on peat in Stafford by Scott Wilson Kirkpatrick and Partners[56] compared the performance under construction traffic of three layer thicknesses on a non-woven membrane and on a plastic mesh. While fill layers of 500 and 750 mm performed satisfactorily, a thickness of 300 mm failed and required an additional overlay of fabric plus 150 mm of aggregate to restore it to traffic. In these applications, topsoil and vegetation are normally left intact and only large stones and shrubs are removed from the area to be covered. It is of course essential to prevent equipment operating directly on the fabric and to prevent damage to the top layer of soil.

The ability of a fabric to prevent punching in of overlying stone has been utilised in permanent road construction, e.g. Leicester section of M69 and Abergavenny Eastern Bypass, where low strength subgrades in cutting required rock blankets to be placed beneath the sub-base. In both instances comparable lengths of subgrade which were not covered with fabrics illustrated the effectiveness of fabric in reducing the required volumes of rock fill.

The use of fabrics as a replacement for part of the sub-base in road pavements has been suggested; clearly pavement deformations are unlikely to be sufficient to utilise the fabric as a reinforcing element but its presence should ensure that overlying granular layers retain their drainage capacity and remain non-frost susceptible.

Fabrics have been placed beneath embankments on soft ground to enhance stability. It is claimed that by applying a horizontal constraint to the ground surface, lateral spread is reduced together with pore-water pressure build up and long term settlements. In an experiment in The Netherlands conducted jointly by Koninklijke Wegenbouw Stevin BV and Akzo Research Laboratories Arnhem, two sand embankments were constructed on soil of low bearing capacity, and beneath one a woven fabric was installed. The reinforced embankment was built to 4·5 m in four days without problems whereas the unreinforced embankment failed at a height of 3·5 m; this suggests that the fabric absorbed substantial loads and acted as a tensile layer.

In both the temporary and permanent drainage of earthworks, fibre fabrics are being used increasingly. Conventionally, a graded granular material is placed in a drainage trench to meet the somewhat conflicting requirements of filtration and hydraulic conductivity. By lining the trench with a fabric to provide filtration the granular backfill's function is reduced to one of hydraulic conductor for which its specification is far less stringent. Fabrics have been used as a complete drain wrapping in this way on the Northampton Southern Bypass. In another application, fabric has been used to cap conventional drains to prevent ingress of topsoil, e.g. A40, Witney.

Low cost impermeable membranes represent another important group of new materials in earthworks. Their use in subgrade protection is discussed subsequently. An impermeable membrane placed on a subgrade, however, only protects the underlying soil from water intrusion from above. By sealing the underside of a compacted fine grained soil layer and so protecting it from surface and subsurface water ingress the soil's suction and hence shear strength can be retained. This forms the basis of the technique of membrane-encapsulated soil layers (MESL) which has been tried with success at the US Army Engineer Waterways Experimental Station. A 300 mm soil layer compacted to 95 % of AASHO-TN80 density on a 6 mm polythene sheet and overlain by an upper membrane of asphalt polypropylene was shown to be capable of supporting military trucks, Sale et al.[57]

SUBGRADE

Material in the traffic-stressed zone has to meet different requirements to those met by the bulk fill materials because of the essential difference in loading. Gravity stresses in the subgrade are low, resulting only from pavement load which Croney[4] suggests will not exceed $12 \, \text{kN m}^{-2}$. However, the subgrade has to sustain repeated stressing from traffic loads without rupture and without large recoverable and irrecoverable deformations.

The magnitude of the traffic stresses depend on contact pressures and contact areas for commercial vehicles and on the pavement design, as discussed in ref. 69. Increased strength and thickness of pavement layers, required to avoid their fatigue failure, have resulted in reduced traffic stresses at the subgrade. Croney[4] quotes $20 \, \text{kN m}^{-2}$ as a typical vertical stress at subgrade level. During construction of the pavement layers, the subgrade must sustain considerably higher traffic stresses and the need to remain stable under this construction loading may, in fact, be the governing criterion for subgrade performance.

Material properties within an embankment and its foundation generally improve after construction as a result of consolidation. At the low stress levels in the subgrade, such improvement is less likely to take place; instead there is greater potential for deterioration as a result of increase in moisture content. Subgrades, therefore, require protection from water by drainage and waterproofing the pavement and shoulders. In addition they should be rendered insensitive to moisture by compaction, stabilisation and chemical treatments.

The use of sub-soil drains in subgrades is now more-or-less standard practice. Methods for calculating the drawdown they produce, have been presented by Russam[58] while Farrar[59] has demonstrated their effectiveness even in heavy clays. Croney[4] recommends that they should be designed to achieve a drawdown to 1 m below formation level and should be placed to get maximum drawdown under the slow lane.

Compaction of the subgrade on embankments is automatically performed and in the Department of Transport Specification[3] no distinction is made between the compaction requirements for the subgrade and the bulk fill. Subgrades in cutting may require densification; since the depth of influence of traffic vibration is large, a depth of up to 1·5 m below formation level may require compaction. Methods for achieving this are now available, e.g. heavy vibratory rollers or dynamic compaction, Menard.[60] With dynamic methods, the lack of compaction at the edges and at the surface must be appreciated in its specification, together with the compliance problem if the surface layer is too soft.

Protection of the subgrade from damage by construction traffic has already been discussed. Additional protection from weather should not be necessary provided that the surface is shaped to drain readily and that laying of the sub-base immediately follows final preparation of the subgrade. Where this has not been possible, surface dressing has been carried out, Croney.[4] Impermeable sheeting, polythene or PVC now provides an alternative method of protection.

Chemical Stabilisation of Subgrades

Occasionally, difficult subgrade materials can be improved by mixing with chemicals. There have only been limited recent developments in chemical stabilisation, and these have been mainly associated with cement and lime;

although it has been shown that other chemicals, such as calcium chloride and lignin, can improve the workability of many soils. Soil–cement has been widely used in sub-bases, but less frequently in subgrades. This material can give problems due to shrinkage and cracking, as reviewed by Kemp[61] and discussed by Williams.[70] Stabilisation with lime can significantly improve plastic subgrades by reducing the soil's plasticity, and an example of its use with montmorillonite-rich black cotton soil in India has been given by Chadda.[62] Not only does the lime improve the workability of the soil, but it also increases the subgrade-bearing capacity thereby reducing the required pavement thickness. For example, Chadda quotes an increase in soaked CBR from 1·5 with no lime to 12·6 with 5 % lime.

Design Parameters

The subgrade material parameters required for any pavement design method should define the material behaviour for the range of conditions in which it exists during the life of the pavement. Ideally, therefore, the parameters should be measured on samples which have been brought from their initial conditions through the effective stress changes, including cycles of wetting and drying, which lead to the effective stress state that will exist beneath the completed pavement.

The initial conditions can differ markedly for soil from a cutting subgrade compared to soil from an embankment subgrade. While depending on the subgrade treatment given, the former could be largely undisturbed, fully saturated, and under high suction, while the latter will be remoulded, partially saturated and under much lower suction. The final equilibrium conditions under the completed pavement depend mainly on the position of the water-table, which in turn is controlled by the sub-soil drainage and soil permeability. Since the soil at subgrade level generally lies above the water table, the pore pressures are less than atmospheric.

Road engineers have preferred to determine design parameters on material brought to the appropriate moisture content, i.e. the equilibrium moisture content (emc), rather than to the appropriate effective stress. A rational method for predicting emc has been developed by TRRL,[63] based on the thermodynamic theory of equilibrium distribution of a liquid in a porous body. The method is outlined in Fig. 5; it embodies three principles:

(i) pore-water pressure, u, depends solely on height above ground water level;

(ii) u is related to suction, s by

$$s = u - \alpha p$$

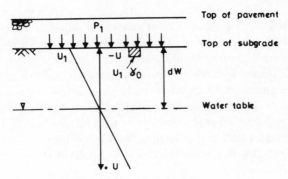

(i)   Equilibrium conditions

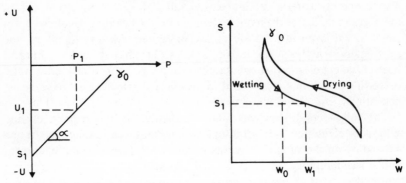

(ii) Pore pressure-applied stress relationship

(iii) Suction-moisture content relationship

FIG. 5.   Method for predicting equilibrium moisture content. Procedure: (a) Estimate depth to water table below subgrade dW. (b) Calculate negative pore pressure U_1 using dW and assuming no moisture transfer under completed impervious pavement. (c) Calculate applied stresses due to pavement, P_1. (d) Read off from (ii) the value of U corresponding to $P = 0$, i.e. S_1, by projecting back from (U_1, P_1) a line of slope α. S_1 is the soil suction. (e) Read off from (iii) the value of equilibrium moisture content, W_1 corresponding to S_1. To follow the correct path, i.e. wetting or drying it is necessary to take account of the initial water content W_0.

Key: $U =$ pore pressure; $P =$ applied stress; $\alpha =$ compressibility factor; $S =$ soil suction: $W =$ moisture content; $\gamma =$ density.

where s is the pore-water pressure in an undisturbed sample relieved from all external stress, p is the external stress, and α is the compressibility factor or slope of the relationship between applied pressure and pore-water pressure;

(iii) s is related to moisture content.

Limitations of the method and the conditions necessary for equilibrium to be reached are reviewed in OECD.[64] The method is examined in more detail by Croney[4] who describes techniques for determining the suction/moisture content relationship. This relationship depends on a number of factors including soil type, porosity, and whether the soil is wetting or drying, or starting from initial saturation or not. As a result, emc is dependent on the moisture content at the time of compaction since this determines both the density and the suction/moisture content path to be followed, i.e. wetting or drying. Figure 6 indicates how it is possible for soils to arrive at different emc despite identical equilibrium stresses. In Fig. 6(i), samples A and B are compacted at different water content but to the same density; assuming the same suction/moisture content relation, sample A will wet up to the equilibrium suction, S_C, while sample B will dry. In Figure 6(ii), samples D and E are compacted at different moisture contents to different densities. Although both have similar suctions, S_D and S_E, and both dry to the equilibrium suction, S_C, they reach different emc's because their different densities give rise to different suction/moisture content relationships.

Empirical methods for predicting emc are discussed in OECD.[64] Clearly those methods which relate emc simply to, say, plastic limit can be faulted. Escario[65] advocates the direct measurement of emc and describes an apparatus for this.

In current UK practice the recommendations given in Road Note No. 29[66] are followed in the design of a new road pavement, see ref. 69. For both flexible and concrete construction the overall pavement thickness depends on the engineers estimate of subgrade and traffic conditions. Traffic is defined in terms of the cumulative equivalent number of standard axles (8200 kg axles) which is determined by considering the initial commercial traffic, the growth rate and the design life of the pavement. Subgrade condition is assessed on the CBR which is an indirect measure of soil strength.

Reference to Fig. 7 which is based on information given in Road Note No. 29[66] indicates the sensitivity of sub-base thickness for a flexible pavement to CBR and demonstrates the need for accurate prediction of this

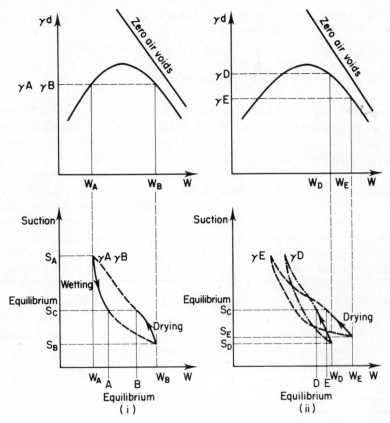

FIG. 6.   Dependence of equilibrium moisture content on compaction moisture content.

parameter. Estimated values of CBR are given in Table 3 of Road Note No. 29 having been based on a procedure described by Black.[67] Direct measurement of CBR should be made in accordance with the procedures given in Test 15 BS 1377.[68]

CBR is strongly dependent on density and water content. This can be seen clearly in Fig. 8 which illustrates that on the dry side of optimum, the CBR is controlled by density, while on the wet side moisture content dominates. Its measurement for wet cohesive soils is not entirely reliable however because of the influence of the method of sample preparation and compaction. For example, it is now appreciated that pore-water pressures may be set up by compaction which, if not allowed to dissipate, may reduce

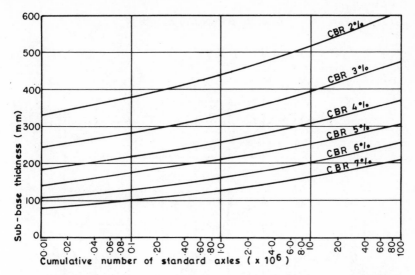

FIG. 7. Effect of predicted traffic density and subgrade CBR value on sub-base thickness requirements for a flexible pavement. *Note:* This figure is based on Road Note 29[66] and should not be used for pavement design without reference to it.

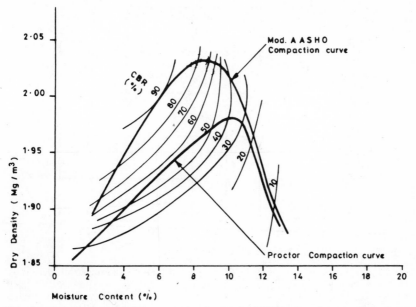

FIG. 8. Standard compaction curves and unsoaked CBR values for a medium/fine silty sand subgrade soil under an airfield pavement in the Sudan.

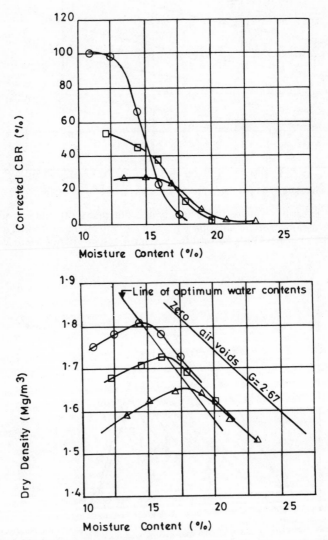

FIG. 9. An example of reduced CBR produced by heavy compaction of a sandy clay. Key: Number of blows/layer: $\triangle$ = 12, $\square$ = 26, $\bigcirc$ = 55.

the soil's bearing capacity. Since increased compaction would correlate with higher pore-water pressures it is possible to produce at the same water content samples with increasing density which have reducing CBR, see Fig. 9.

It is not very practicable to bring CBR specimens of the appropriate density and structure (i.e. undisturbed or remoulded) to the estimated equilibrium effective stress state. Croney[4] recommends, therefore, that remoulded samples should be compacted to the estimated final density at several moisture contents and the pore pressure measured for each; by extrapolation, the CBR at the equilibrium pore pressure can be deduced. An alternative approach has been to assume that the relevant CBR can be measured on a sample compacted to the likely final density and emc.

Preparation of a sample at the predicted emc may be sufficient for strength and hence CBR measurements on compacted soils. However, for the stress–strain parameters which would be required for a structural approach to pavement design, see ref. 71, such a method of sample preparation would not be adequate.

The use of a measure of bearing capacity in pavement design seems illogical when the low stresses at subgrade are considered. A structural approach to design is clearly more attractive. However, measurement of the relevant deformation parameters is a formidable task in view both of their dependence on stress path and stress history and of the difficulties of testing at the appropriate stress levels. These problems are discussed by Brown.[71] In any method of design, it is essential to recognise the wide variation in subgrade conditions which will arise, despite controlled construction.

REFERENCES

1. LEWIS, W. A. and PARSONS, A. W. *Proc. ICE*, **54**, 425, August 1973.
2. LEFLAIVE, E. *Hwys and Road Const.*, **43**, 14, October 1975.
3. DEPARTMENT OF TRANSPORT. Specification for road and bridges work, HMSO, London, 1976.
4. CRONEY, D. The design and performance of road pavements, HMSO, London, 1977.
5. SKEMPTON, A. W. and HUTCHINSON, J. N. State of the art report, Proc. 7th ICSMFE, 261, 1969.
6. SARMA, S. K. *Geotechnique*, **23**, 423, 1973.
7. HUTCHINSON, J. N. General Report: Theme 3. Symposium of the IAEG, 1977.
8. EARLY, K. R. and SKEMPTON, A. W. *Qrtly J. Engrg Glgy*, **5**, 19, 1972.
9. CHANDLER, R. J., PACHAKIS, M., MERCER, J. and WRIGHTMAN, J. *Qrtly J. Engrg Glgy*, **6**, 405, 1973.

10. SKEMPTON, A. W. *Geotechnique*, **14**, 77, 1964.
11. VAUGHAN, P. R. and WALBANCKE, H. J. *Geotechnique*, **23**, 531, 1973.
12. COCKSEDGE, J. E. and HIGHT, D. W. *Artesian conditions in glaciated landscapes and their influence on the stability of road cuttings*, 1977 (to be published).
13. CASHMAN, P. M. and HAWS, E. T. ICE Conf. Ground. Engrg, 1970.
14. SYMONS, I. F. TRRL Report LR 711, Crowthorne, 1976.
15. BISHOP, A. W. and GREEN, P. A. *Proc. Conf. on field instrumentation in geotechnical engineering*, 13, Butterworths, London, 1974.
16. ROWE, P. W. *Geotechnique*, **14**, 321, 1964.
17. ROWE, P. W. *Geotechnique*, **22**, 195, 1972.
18. WROTH, C. P. and SIMPSON, B. Proc. speciality conference on performance of earth and earth-supported structures, Purdue University, 1972.
19. MURRAY, R. T. TRRL Report LR 419, Crowthorne, 1971.
20. MURRAY, R. T. TRRL Report LR 617, Crowthorne, 1974.
21. *Proc. Conf. on field instrumentation in geotechnical engineering*, Butterworths, London, 1974.
22. MCKENNA, J. M., EYRE, W. A. and WOLSTENHOLME, D. R. *Geotechnique*, **25**, 51, 1975.
23. DE BEER, E. E., WALLAYS, M. G. G., PAQUAY, J. J. and VEILLEN, A. R. M. Proc. 8th ICSMFE **2.2**, 31, 1973.
24. MENARD, L. and BROISE, Y. *Geotechnique*, **25**, 3, 1975.
25. SNEDKER, E. A. *Hwys Design and Const.*, 2, January 1973.
26. FARRAR, D. M. and DARLEY, P. TRRL Report LR 688, Crowthorne, 1975.
27. RODIN, S. *Civ. Eng. Pub. Wks Review*, **60**, 197, 1965.
28. COCKSEDGE, J. E. and HIGHT, D. W. Proc. Symposium 'The engineering behaviour of glacial materials; 220, Univ. of Birmingham, 1975.
29. NORMAN, R. CIRIA, Research Report, **3**, 1965.
30. FARRAR, D. M. TRRL Report LR 406, Crowthrone, 1971.
31. DENNEHY, J. P. M.Phil. thesis 1976, Univ. of Surrey, Guildford (work carried out by Ground Engineering Limited, funded by John Laing and Sons).
32. OECD ROAD RESEARCH GROUP. 'Water in roads: methods for determining soil moisture content and pore water tension', 1973.
33. PARSONS, A. W. TRRL Report LR 750, Crowthorne, 1976.
34. VAUGHAN, P. R., LOVENBURY, H. T. and HORSWILL, P. *Geotechnique*, **25**, 555, 1975.
35. PENMAN, ADM Symposium on 'Rock mechanics in highway construction', Inst. Hwy Engrs, London and Univ. of Newcastle-upon-Tyne, 1971.
36. MITCHELL, P. B. and MAGUIRE, F. J. *Civ. Eng. Pub. Wks Review*, **63**, 1217, 1968.
37. PARSONS, A. W. TRRL Report LR 112, Crowthorne, 1967.
38. INGOLDBY, H. C. and PARSONS, A. W. TRRL Report LR 806, Crowthorne, 1977.
39. SHAMBURGER, J. H., PATRICK, D. M. and LUTTEN, R. J. Interim Report No. FHWA-RD-75-61, Federal Highway Administration, Washington, 1975.
40. KENNARD, M. F., KNILL, J. L. and VAUGHAN, P. R. *Qrtly J. Engrg Glgy*, **1**, 3, 1967.
41. VAUGHAN, P. R. *Proc. ICE*, **55**, 697, September, 1973.
42. SHERWOOD, P. T. TRRL Report LR 647, Crowthorne, 1974.
43. SHERWOOD, P. T. TRRL Report LR 649, Crowthorne, 1975.

44. SHERWOOD, P. T. TRRL Report LR 686, Crowthorne, 1975.
45. ROE, P. G. TRRL Report LR 728, Crowthorne, 1976.
46. SUTHERLAND, H. B., FINLAY, T. W. and CRAM, I. A. *J. Inst. Hwy Engrs*, 1, June 1968.
47. MCKECHNIE THOMSON, G. and RODIN, S. *Proc. ICE*, 55, 677, 1973.
48. SHERWOOD, P. T. and RYLEY, M. D. TRRL Report LR 324, Crowthorne, 1970.
49. LINDSAY, J. F. *Civ. Eng. Pub. Wks Review*, **65**, 1285, 1970.
50. RODIN, S. *Ground Engrg*, **4**, 19, January 1971.
51. MCLAREN, D. TRRL Report LR 238, Crowthorne, 1968.
52. HUANG, Y. H. and SHEPARD, F. D. *Highway Research Record*, **223**, 45, 1968.
53. VIDAL, H. *Highway Research Record*, **282**, 1, 1969.
54. Int. conf. 'The use of fabrics in geotechnics'. Ecole Nationale des Ponts et Chaussees, Paris, 1977.
55. MCGOWN, A. and OZELTON, M. W. *Civ. Eng. Pub. Wks Review*, **68**, 25, 1973.
56. SCOTT WILSON KIRKPATRICK AND PARTNERS. 'Staffordshire County Council Stafford inner relief road'. Scott Wilson Kirkpatrick and Partners, Basingstoke, 1975.
57. SALE, J. P., PARKER, F. and BARKER, W. R. *Proc. ASCE, Soil Mech. and Fdn. Eng. Div.*, **99**, SM12, 1077, December 1973.
58. RUSSAM, K. TRRL Report LR 110, Crowthorne, 1967.
59. FARRAR, D. M. TRRL Report LR 186, Crowthorne, 1968.
60. MENARD, L. *Travaux*, **54**, 56, November 1972.
61. KEMP, W. R. 'Shrinkage and cracking of soil–cement: a review', M.Sc. Dissertation, Department of Civil Engineering, The Univ. of Leeds.
62. CHADDA, L. R. *Roads and Road Const.*, 177, June 1970.
63. BLACK, W. P. M., CRONEY, D. and JACOBS, J. C. Tech. Paper 41, Road Research Laboratory, 1958.
64. OECD ROAD RESEARCH GROUP. 'Water in roads: prediction of moisture content of road subgrades', 1973.
65. ESCARIO, V. Conf. on expansive soils, Texas, 1969.
66. TRRL. Road Note RN 29, Crowthorne, 1970.
67. BLACK, W. P. M. *Geotechnique*, 12, 271, 1962.
68. BS 1377. British Standards Institution, London, 1975.
69. PEATTIE, K. R. Flexible pavement design, Chapter 1, in *Developments in Highway Pavement Engineering*—1, P. S. Pell (ed.), Applied Science Publishers, London, 1978.
70. WILLIAMS, R. I. T. Cement stabilised materials, Chapter 1, in *Developments in Highway Pavement Engineering*—1, P. S. Pell (ed.), Applied Science Publishers, London, 1978.
71. BROWN, S. F. Material characteristics for analytical pavement design, Chapter 2, in *Developments in Highway Pavement Engineering*—1, P. S. Pell (ed.), Applied Science Publishers, London, 1978.

Chapter 2

AGGREGATES IN BASE CONSTRUCTION

J. W. FRY

E.C.C. Quarries Ltd, Exeter, UK

SUMMARY

The road construction programme has resulted in high capital expenditure in the quarrying industry to modernise plants to cope with the high aggregate demand. The metrication of the industry has caused few problems except for some single-sized aggregates.

The chapter discusses the revisions which have taken place in the 'Specification for road and bridge works' since the 1963 edition, for granular sub-bases and roadbases, and the effect these have had on the materials.

Some problems associated with wet-mix macadam are discussed and suggestions made to overcome them.

The uses of two waste materials, colliery shale and china clay sand, which occur in large quantities are described.

Aggregate, either coarse or fine but generally a combination of the two, is used in all layers of a road pavement bound by bituminous or cementitious binders, or unbound. The road construction programme has called for large quantities of material which has caused the quarrying industry to undertake extensive expansion and modernisation schemes with high capital expenditure in order to meet this demand. More recently the metrication of the industry has been completed so that all relevant British Standards and the 'Specification for road and bridge works'[1] have been published in metric units. The changeover has in fact caused very little disruption to the running of the industry and the aggregates are the same today as they were before. There are, however, a few anomalies which have arisen due entirely to the selection of the metric sieve sizes used for testing the grading of aggregates. The two sieves causing the most concern are the 28 mm in place of the 1 in sieve and the 14 mm in place of the $\frac{1}{2}$ in sieve. In both cases the increase in aperture size has been in excess of 10%. When considering continuously graded aggregates little problems are encountered as adjustments can be made to blending proportion. In the case of a single-sized aggregate, as used for precoated chippings, a sample tested on metric sieves can be unacceptable whereas the same sample would be acceptable if the equivalent imperial sieves were used. Fortunately this anomalous position is recognised and allowance being made accordingly. There are, however, pressures from some users of roadstone to produce more stringent specifications for certain uses, such as for surface dressing treatments. This could cause economic repercussions if large quantities of substantially altered chippings were to be required. Aggregates used in the bound layers of a pavement have been mentioned in the previous book in this series. The developments in unbound sub-bases and roadbases and the use of some waste products will be considered in this chapter.

GRANULAR SUB-BASE TYPE 1

The introduction of the fourth edition of the 'Specification for road and bridge works' modified the grading requirements of the third edition by slightly tightening the grading with the inclusion of the $\frac{3}{8}$ in (10 mm) sieve and at the same time permitting the percentage passing the 200 mesh (75 μm) sieve to be increased to a maximum of 10%. A comparison of the grading requirements is shown in Table 1. To safeguard against the inclusion of clay fines, the aggregate passing the 36 mesh (425 μm) sieve when tested in accordance with BS 1377[2] has to be non-plastic. At the same

TABLE 1
GRANULAR SUB-BASE TYPE 1 GRADING COMPARISON

BS sieve		% passing	
Imperial	Metric	3rd edition	5th edition
3 in	75 mm	100	100
$1\frac{1}{2}$ in	37·5 mm	85–100	85–100
$\frac{3}{8}$ in	10 mm		40–70
$\frac{3}{16}$ in	5 mm	25–45	25–45
No. 25	600 μm	8–22	8–22
No. 200	75 μm	0–2	0–10

time limitations on the moisture content were removed. The fifth edition of the Specification has included a minimum 10% fines value of 5 for all aggregates except well burnt non-plastic shale. The effects of these modifications are difficult to evaluate but they have resulted in some benefits to both the supplying and contracting sides of the construction industry. Crusher Run materials which previously did not satisfy the 2% maximum passing the 75 μm sieve are now within specification. This has consequently increased the potential sources of supply to the industry. However, the continued use of the test for plasticity detailed in BS 1377 does cause problems at times, particularly when crushed limestone is being tested.

The removal of the limits on moisture content have enabled the suppliers to deliver either dry material direct from the crushing plant or from stockpiles. Under most conditions the latter material should not have a moisture content in excess of 5%, unless the aggregate has a high water absorption, due to the natural drainage characteristic of the sub-base.

If the sub-base is supplied dry then the contractor is likely to benefit as the compacted density will generally be lower than if there is moisture in the aggregate. This will of course help the sub-base to perform one of the

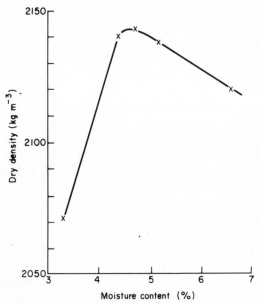

FIG. 1.   Dry density/moisture content curve for a crushed limestone.

functions for which it is intended, that of a drainage layer. On the other hand for a maximum structural contribution to the pavement the denser the sub-base the better.

There is thus a conflict in performance characteristics of the sub-base and it is suggested that the structural contribution is of greater importance in the construction of a sound road pavement. The variation in dry density with varying moisture content is shown in Fig. 1.

GRANULAR SUB-BASE TYPE 2

The modifications since the third edition of the 'Specification for road and bridge works' have been to specify the moisture content of the sub-base more precisely by use of the vibrating hammer test in BS 1377, to limit the plasticity index to less than 6, and to permit the use of well burnt non-plastic shale. A minimum limit of 5 has recently been placed on the 10 % fines value of the aggregate except for well burnt non-plastic shale.

The use of Type 2 sub-base tended to increase in recent years. This is due to its permitted use in the full depth of sub-base, provided the California Bearing Ratio (CBR) value is adequate for the traffic loading, and that it is generally cheaper than a Type 1 sub-base. It has been found that most Type 2 materials are affected by adverse weather conditions and extensive delays can be experienced in prolonged periods of rain. To avoid this it is better to use the Type 2 in the lower layer of the sub-base.

ROADBASE MACADAMS

The two materials under consideration are wet-mix and dry-bound macadams. The use of dry-bound macadam has generally declined in the past few years in favour of wet-mix macadam. This has no doubt been due to the relative problems experienced in the laying of dry-bound macadam which is slow, labour intensive, and dependent on dry aggregates to obtain a satisfactory base.

Wet-mix can be laid at high daily tonnages to accurate level using a conventional paving machine or spreader box. One of the problems which does occur with wet-mix is the segregation which takes place during transportation of the material to site. This produces a fairly regular pattern on the laid material of slightly coarser patches which coincide with the end of each load delivered. This can be overcome to a great extent by ensuring that the grading of the aggregate is maintained at the fine end of the limits shown in Table 2. Additionally the use of 28 mm nominal sized aggregate as the largest size used in the macadam will also improve the problem. If 40 mm nominal sized aggregate is used it has been found that a shift of 5 % finer on the 5 mm sieve and above has produced a uniform macadam and a durable pavement. In this particular case the aggregate used was a crushed limestone.

TABLE 2
WET-MIX MACADAM GRADING
REQUIREMENT

BS sieve	% passing by mass
50 mm	100
37·5 mm	95–100
20 mm	60–80
10 mm	40–60
5 mm	25–40
2·36 mm	15–30
600 μm	8–22
75 μm	0–8

Whatever method is used to reduce the tendency for segregation to occur by far the most important factor in producing a good wet-mix macadam is consistency in grading and uniform distribution of the water addition. One interesting omission from both the fourth and fifth editions of the 'Specification for road and bridge works', is any mention of a mixer being used to produce the macadam. This was formally subject to the approval of the engineer and it does seem an illogical relaxation of the Specification.

It is to be hoped that the majority of the wet-mix used has been produced through a mixing plant with some means of controlling the amount of added water. But in the absence of any specific obligation it has been known that a spray bar on a conveyor belt or even a hose-pipe has been considered as adequate means of adding water and relying on the mixing taking place while the macadam is being loaded into lorries and being laid.

At the present time there is a tendency for doubt to be cast on the suitability of wet-mix macadam for use on roads designed to Road Note 29.[3] If this were true then all such roads should have failed and this is patently not the case. It is essential that good control of quality is maintained throughout the production of a roadbase of wet-mix. If the macadam is well made, well laid, and properly compacted the result will be a durable roadbase, provided that the underlying materials are satisfactory and adequate for the design of the pavement.

WASTE MATERIALS

When suitable waste materials are available it is advantageous to use them. As well as giving an economic advantage by means of reduced cost, the resource of valuable good quality aggregate is preserved and the removal of unsightly waste tips can improve the environment.

Colliery shale is produced in large quantities as a by-product of the coalmining industry. It is reported by Sherwood[4] that about 50 million tonnes are produced annually from existing coal mines. About 6 million tonnes is used annually, the majority of it in road construction.

The major part of this annual consumption is used as fill material in both the burnt and unburnt state. In the past it had been considered that the unburnt shale was liable to spontaneous combustion and was therefore considered unsuitable. It has been shown in practice that unburnt shale when properly compacted in accordance with Clause 608 of the Specification is quite satisfactory and not liable to spontaneous combustion.

The use of burnt colliery shale is permitted as both a Type 1 and Type 2 granular sub-base material. There is, however, likely to be a restriction on the use of these materials within 450 mm of the road surface as the majority of burnt shales are reported as being frost-susceptible. The frost resistance can be improved to acceptable limits by the addition of cement, see Chapter 3. This, however, increases the cost of the material quite substantially and the economic advantages may be lost. The results of tests carried out on burnt colliery shale are shown in Table 3 and the extent of the improvement obtained in the frost resistance with the addition of 5 % cement can be seen. With the incorporation of cement the material would then become cement stabilised, see ref. 5, and would have to comply with the requirements of either Clause 805 soil cement or cement-bound granular material to Clause 806. The results of compressive strength tests on some burnt shales with the addition of 10 % cement are shown in Table 4, and the results of tests carried out on unburnt shale with varying cement contents are shown in Table 5. These indicate that the strength requirement for Clause 805 of $2.8 \, \text{N mm}^{-2}$ for cylindrical specimens can readily be met. The strength requirement for Clause 806 is the same.

Pulverised fuel ash (PFA) has been extensively used as a fill material, the

TABLE 3

THE EFFECT OF CEMENT ADDITION TO THE FROST HEAVE OF BURNT COLLIERY SHALE[4]

Shale no.	Retained 20 mm BS sieve (%)	Natural moisture content (%)	Frost heave (mm)	
			without cement	with 5% cement
1	26	11	22	7
2	10	20	41	13
3	25	17	45	11
4	13	14	30	8
5	49	8	6	—

TABLE 4

COMPRESSIVE STRENGTH TESTS ON CYLINDRICAL SAMPLES OF BURNT COLLIERY SHALE CONTAINING 10% CEMENT[4]

Shale	Moisture content (%)	Compacted dry density ($Mg\,m^{-3}$)	7-day compressive strength ($N\,mm^{-2}$)
1	12·0	1·76	4·70
2	11·7	1·81	6·60
3	12·6	1·76	6·80
4	12·1	1·76	6·80
5	10·4	1·83	6·65
6	11·4	1·74	6·45

TABLE 5

7-DAY COMPRESSIVE STRENGTH TESTS ON CYLINDRICAL SAMPLES OF UNBURNT SHALE STABILISED WITH CEMENT[4]

Shale	Moisture content (%)	Compressive strength in $N\,mm^{-2}$ Cement contents		
		4%	8%	12%
1	6	2·28	3·24	3·56
	7	2·68	4·00	5·65
2	6	2·83	5·90	7·31
	7	2·80	5·55	7·41

TABLE 6
7-DAY COMPRESSIVE STRENGTH OF CEMENT
STABILISED CHINA CLAY SAND

Cement content (%)	Compressive strength cubes ($N\,mm^{-2}$)	cores ($N\,mm^{-2}$)
4	7·0	9
5·3	9·0	—
6·0	11·0	10·5

relatively low bulk density of the compacted PFA being of considerable advantage when the material is used on highly compressible soils. The fineness of the PFA prevents its use as either a Type 1 or Type 2 sub-base, but it will generally satisfy the grading requirement of Clause 805 soil cement. The economics of cement stabilisation must therefore be considered in determining the use of PFA in the sub-base of a road, while for minor roads there is the possibility of using this material for the roadbase.

In Devon and Cornwall large quantities of waste are generated during the extraction of china clay. For every tonne of china clay produced, approximately 3·7 tonnes of coarse sand occurs as a by-product and this is the material which has potential for use in road construction. The composition of the sand is mainly quartz with varying quantities of feldspar, tourmaline, and mica, depending on the pit from which it was extracted. The sand produces extremely stable fill areas and density of compacted material is normally in the range 1·9 to 2·2 tonnes m^{-3}.

The frost susceptibility test has been carried out on china clay sand from several sources and the material is rated non-susceptible except when the minus 75 μm proportion has exceeded 10%. In the latter case it was rated marginally susceptible.

The sand is suitable for use as Type 2 granular sub-base although careful selection of material to comply with the grading requirements is necessary as the percentage passing the 5 mm sieve tends to be too high from some tips. As with other Type 2 materials the sand is affected by adverse weather conditions when laid in thin layers. The china clay sand is suitable for use as cement stabilised material to Clauses 805 soil cement or 806 cement-bound granular material. Table 6 shows that adequate strength can be obtained to satisfy the requirements of these clauses. These results were obtained from site trials.

REFERENCES

1. DEPARTMENT OF TRANSPORT. Specification for road and bridge works, HMSO, London, 1976.
2. BS 1377. Methods of test for soils for civil engineering purposes, British Standards Institution, London, 1975.
3. ROAD RESEARCH LABORATORY. A guide to the structural design of pavements for new roads, Road Note No. 29, 3rd ed., Department of the Environment, HMSO, London, 1970.
4. SHERWOOD, P. T. The use of waste and low-grade materials in road construction: 2. Colliery shale, TRRL Report LR 649, Dept. of the Environment, Transport and Road Research Laboratory, Crowthorne, 1975.
5. WILLIAMS, R. I. T. Cement stabilised materials, Chapter 5, in *Developments in Highway Pavement Engineering*—1, P. S. Pell (ed.), Applied Science Publishers, London, 1978.

Chapter 3

FROST HEAVE DAMAGE AND ITS PREVENTION

R. H. JONES

The University of Nottingham, UK

SUMMARY

Frost heaving and associated thaw weakening arising from a combination of freezing temperatures, frost susceptible materials and the availability of water, cause loss of riding quality and possible permanent damage to roads. The mechanism of the heaving process is reviewed and recent developments in mathematical models presented.

Methods of assessing frost susceptibility are examined critically. Both direct tests, including the proposed revision to the TRRL test to accommodate self refrigerating units and indirect assessments, with particular reference to the role of suction characteristics, are discussed.

A framework is proposed for a revised design procedure in which the ground water level and the capillarity and permeability of the subgrade are considered.

Whilst the chapter is orientated towards British conditions and problems with unbound materials, much of the content is of general application.

INTRODUCTION

Frost heaving and associated thaw weakening can cause loss of riding quality and permanent damage to roads. Freezing temperatures, frost susceptible materials and a supply of water are the necessary prerequisites for frost heave. In Britain, the maximum depth of frost penetration is approximately 0·5 m, so that the materials mainly affected are those in unbound bases and sub-bases. Overseas, where deeper frost penetrations or

43

even permafrost conditions prevail, the overriding interest in subgrades and soils generally is reflected in recent symposia.[1,2]

Damage is associated particularly with differential heave, e.g. between the pavement and edge beams leading to transverse cracking, and with thaw weakening resulting from the loss of bearing capacity due to the excess water content. Under British conditions, difficulties have usually occurred[3] only as follows:

(1) with roads whose structure was old or already inadequate for its traffic;
(2) where poor quality limestone sub-base was used (particularly in association with high stone content asphalt surfacing);
(3) on chalk sub-bases or subgrades.

Heave, measured under standard conditions in the TRRL test, is taken as the characteristic parameter of frost susceptibility. There is an obvious parallel between this value and differential heave and the relationship between total and differential settlement of foundations. Furthermore, the 'total' heave is a measure of the water available to cause thaw weakening.

Under site conditions the heave is governed by environmental factors (climate and availability of water) and the material properties (e.g. pore size distribution). Currently, in England and Wales only materials which heave less than 13 mm in the TRRL test are acceptable in the top 450 mm.[4] In Scotland, where all the testing is done at one approved centre, provided the surface is impermeable and the drainage good[5] the corresponding value is 18 mm. Many (particularly amongst contractors and suppliers) consider that this illogical situation should be resolved by applying the Scottish limits to the whole of the UK.

The above classification and design is based on an empirical correlation between the results of the TRRL test and observations of road behaviour.[6] This method has been criticised because:

(a) the reproducibility of the TRRL test is poor;
(b) the classification is based on tests and observations on subgrades, and may need modification when applied to sub-bases;
(c) local environmental factors are ignored.

Research and development being undertaken to produce improved procedures which will overcome these objections are described in this chapter, commencing with a brief discussion of the relevant background. Consideration is then given to recent developments in mathematical models, proposed revisions to the TRRL test, and to indirect methods of assessing frost susceptibility. The major effects of the water table position and the capillarity and permeability of the subgrade are then discussed. Finally, proposals are made for a revised design procedure, incorporating these effects.

Whilst the chapter is orientated towards British conditions, relevant overseas experience and developments are discussed and much of the current work described is of general application.

THE MECHANISM OF FROST HEAVE

During prolonged freezing spells, the zero isotherm descends through the pavement into the unbound courses and perhaps even into the subgrade. In order to penetrate through the neck of the pores (Fig. 1), the ice must adopt an appropriate radius of curvature, which is associated with a pressure difference across the ice/water interface and a freezing point depression. Unless heave is prevented by the application of the appropriate pressure, the resulting pore water suction will draw water to the freezing front. The consequent heave is much greater than that corresponding to the 9% expansion of *in situ* water, especially when the hydraulic and thermal conditions are such that ice penetration is held up from time to time, resulting in the formation of lenses. Heave is greatest when saturated or near saturated materials freeze in an open system, i.e. with free access to water.

The above capillary model[7–9] assumes that adsorption forces are negligible and represents ideal granular behaviour. Ideal clay behaviour in which all the water is adsorbed[10] is considered later. However, the capillary model, with the pore size reduced if necessary by the thickness of a thin adsorbed film, is an appropriate model for most road pavement materials.

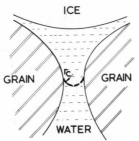

FIG. 1.   Ideal capillary model.

Whilst progress has been made in quantifying this model, to give a numerical prediction of heave, further development is needed before the quantitative model can play its full role in the rational design process described later.

Suction and Freezing Point Depression

Above the water table, water may be held in pores by capillary action or adsorption forces. The amount of water adsorbed depends on the surface activity and specific surface of the particles. Both quantities are much greater for clay minerals than for iso-dimensional minerals (e.g. quartz or calcium carbonate). The lower (Gibbs) free energy of the pore water with respect to bulk water can be expressed as the equivalent suction needed to remove the pore water from the material. The total suction is then the sum of the matrix suction (due to interfacial, gravitational and adsorption forces) and the osmotic suction (due to solutes).

Changes in pressure influence the freezing point according to the equation

$$(V_w \Delta P_w - V_i \Delta P_i) T_0 = \Delta T L \tag{1}$$

where V_w and V_i = specific volumes of water and ice respectively ($m^3 kg^{-1}$), ΔP_w and ΔP_i = changes in water and ice pressures respectively ($kN m^{-2}$), T_0 = 'normal' freezing point (= 273 °K), ΔT = change in freezing point (°C, depression negative), and L = latent heat of fusion (= 336 kJ kg^{-1}).

This equation, for the special case of $\Delta P_i = 0$, reduces to

$$pF = 4 \cdot 095 + \log(-\Delta T) \tag{2}$$

where pF = log (suction expressed in cm of water).[11] Equation (2) gives the matrix suction and both eqns. (1) and (2) refer to stable cooling—they give the highest temperature at which ice can nucleate. Lacking nucleation, there will be supercooling below this temperature.

The Capillary Model of Frost Heave

At the radius of curvature necessary for ice to penetrate the throat between two grains (Fig. 1), the pressure difference across the ice/water interface will be

$$P_i - P_w = \frac{2\sigma_{iw}}{r} \tag{3}$$

where P_i and P_w = pressures in the ice and water phases respectively, σ_{iw} = interfacial energy ice/water ($\simeq 0 \cdot 033 J m^{-2}$),[12] and r = radius of curvature.

Equations (1) and (3) may be combined for $\Delta P_i = P_i = 0$ and hence $\Delta P_w = P_w$ to yield

$$\Delta T = \frac{2\sigma_{iw} T_0 V_w}{rL} \qquad (4)$$

The derivation of eqns. (3) and (4) assumes (a) cylindrical pores with a zero contact angle between ice and water, (b) absence of air and dissolved salts, and (c) a constant ice pressure above the freezing front. The effect of air will be discussed later. Dissolved salt effects will be additive. Since closely adjacent parts of the ice are very unlikely to be under different pressures, the ice will be at overburden pressure.

Thus, for granular materials with a characteristic critical pore radius r_c frost penetration can only occur when

$$P_i - P_w \geq \frac{2\sigma_{iw}}{r_c} \qquad (5)$$

i.e. when the temperature falls to the value given by eqn. (4) when $r = r_c$. If

$$P_i - P_w < \frac{2\sigma_{iw}}{r_c} \qquad (6)$$

an ice lens will be formed.

The capillary model predicts:

(1)   the soil moisture will freeze at a temperature lower than $0\,°C$;
(2)   water remains unfrozen in small pores when larger pores are ice filled at the same temperature;
(3)   at a given instant, water is freezing over a range of depths in the zone known as the freezing front;
(4)   the temperature depression, the suction required for penetration and therefore the tendency for ice segregation all increase with decreasing pore radius;
(5)   water is drawn to the freezing front continuously during both penetration and segregation until final equilibrium is reached under the imposed temperature conditions.

Because water remains unfrozen in the smallest pores at quite low temperatures, frozen ground is slightly permeable to water substance. Recent evidence suggests that there may be ice as well as water movement so that a continuous transverse layer of ice does not form a completely impermeable barrier.[2b] However, due to the low permeability, the additional heave arising from transport within the already frozen material is likely to be significant only in permanently frozen ground.

Adsorbed Water Model
In this ideal clay model all the water is assumed to be held by adsorption forces with the air phase excluded.[10] The adsorbed water will not freeze until the temperature is lowered to that given by eqn. (1) for the appropriate suction. Freezing corresponds to a drying process and will generate suctions which will cause water to flow through the adsorbed films towards the freezing front.

Relationship of Ideal Models to Actual Road Materials
Actual materials likely to be susceptible to frost heaving are shown in Fig. 2. The behaviour of subgrades is likely to be somewhere between the extremes represented by the idealised models of the last two sections. The capillary model can be modified to accommodate an intermediate material having a thin adsorbed film by reducing r_c by the thickness of the film. A soil might be composed of a mixture of coarse particles (having thin adsorbed films) and pockets of clayey materials in which all the water is adsorbed. In

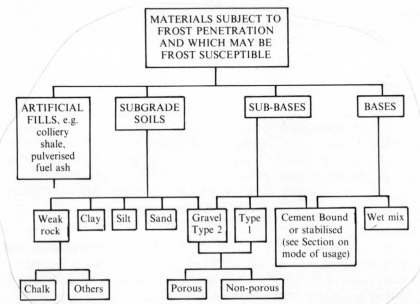

FIG. 2.   Materials subject to frost penetration which may be frost susceptible.

intermediate and mixed materials, the ice formation arises both by pore penetration and by the freezing of adsorbed films. In such materials, water transport through the adsorbed films may be a significant factor, particularly at low degrees of saturation.

The evidence available from calorimetry[9] and dilatometry[10] suggests that the capillary model is realistic for granular materials and even for some clays at low suctions (pF < 4), presumably because of the presence of relatively large pores within the clay. Granular sub-bases (and subgrades of similar composition) are subdivided into porous and non-porous materials. The latter have voids only between the aggregate particles whilst the former also contain voids within the particles themselves[13] which add to the heave.

Heaving Pressures

If the heave is restrained, the freezing process is characterised by the maximum pressure required to prevent heave.

The capillary model predicts:[8]

$$P_{h_{max}} = 2\sigma_{iw}\left(\frac{1}{r_p} + \frac{1}{r_g}\right)\frac{A_i}{A} \qquad (7)$$

where $P_{h_{max}}$ = maximum heaving pressure, r_p = pore radius (entrance), r_g = particle radius, A_i = area of ice/solid contact in the horizontal plane, and A = total horizontal area.

For soil particles r_g/r_p may be taken as 5·6.[8] If a lens forms between two layers of closely packed spheres

$$\frac{A_i}{A} = 0.907$$

so that

$$P_{h_{max}} = \frac{2\cdot14\sigma_{iw}}{r_p} \qquad (8)$$

If the heaving results in the solid particles losing contact with one another, the heaving pressure becomes:

$$P_{h_{max}} = \frac{2\sigma_{iw}}{r_p} \qquad (9)$$

Characterisation of Pore Size

Several methods have been proposed for estimating a single characteristic pore radius, r_c, for a graded non-spherical material.

On the basis of particle size distribution curves, typical particle radii may be taken as $0.5\,D_{10}$ (for well graded materials) and $0.5\,D_{50}$ (for single sized materials), where 10 and 50 % of the particles are smaller than D_{10} and D_{50} respectively. In a recent study, this method, in conjunction with eqn. (8) and $r_p = r_g/5.6$, gave a closer agreement between experiment and theory than either of the air intrusion or suction characteristic methods.[14]

The air intrusion value is the air pressure at which air bubbles through a saturated specimen contained in a pressure chamber,[14,15] r_c is found when the bubbling pressure is inserted in the equation

$$P_a - P_w = \frac{2\sigma_{aw}}{r} \qquad (10)$$

where P_a, P_w = air and water pressure respectively, and σ_{aw} = interfacial energy (air/water).

Finally, a pore size distribution curve can be inferred from the suction moisture content curve, by expressing the moisture content as percentage saturation and converting the suction into an equivalent pore radius using eqn. (10). Since ice intrusion corresponds to a desorption process, this branch of the suction characteristic is used in preference to the adsorption curve.

The Effect of Pore Air on the Frost Heaving Process

Although the discussion of the capillary model assumed saturated conditions, most materials in practice will contain some air. In partially saturated materials, ice should form in the liquid phase since this involves minimum energy (interfacial energies are related $\sigma_{ia}:\sigma_{aw}:\sigma_{iw} = 3.2:2.2:1$). Suction due to the air/water interface will lower the pressure on both ice and water phases. In accordance with eqn. (1) the equilibrium temperature will rise by $0.0073 \times$ suction (bars). Except for very high suctions, this effect can be neglected.

The presence of air will reduce both the permeability and the hydraulic gradient during heave.[9] Even when air is widely spread through the material, frost heaving may still occur due to pores becoming ice saturated.[16] Elsewhere, pores will be depleted of water and remain ice free. The commonly made assumption that heave will only occur if the degree of saturation exceeds 91.7 % (i.e. ice saturation) is thus an oversimplification.

Water Flow Towards a Freezing Front

An adaptation of the Darcy equation was proposed by Ruckli[17] in which

$$\frac{H}{t} = \frac{1.09 P_w k}{l} \qquad (11)$$

where H = heave in time t, P_w = suction at the freezing front, k = coefficient of permeability, and l = distance to the water table.

However, this equation sometimes vastly overestimates the heaving rate[12] mainly because the suction gradient is not uniform but falls rapidly within the freezing front as shown diagrammatically in Fig. 3. Within the front, the flow is controlled by the unsaturated permeability which varies with the applied suction to which the unfrozen water content is related. Whilst the suction permeability characteristic can be determined, reliable direct measurements of suction gradients in the rapidly changing region are unlikely to be obtained. An indirect approach in which heaving rates based on assumed distributions are compared with values obtained in controlled tests (e.g. in the precise freezing cell) is likely to be more successful. One such assumption, currently under examination, that the suction gradient within an advancing freezing front is proportional to the suction (Fig. 3) leads to:

$$h_0 = \frac{k_{\text{unsat}} \text{ at suction } h_m}{k_{\text{sat}}} \cdot h_m$$

However, during ice lensing, h will be less than h_m at the top of the freezing front, and the value of h_0 will be reduced (see the next two sections).

If air is present, still further modifications of eqn. (11) may be required to account for the air filled voids commonly observed in ice lenses.[12,18]

Transient Heat Flow

The equations of heat flow accompanied by water flow for a penetrating frost line are given in Fig. 3. A datum with constant temperature conditions is assumed at depth. Both the surface as it heaves and the level of frost penetration are moving boundaries with respect to time.

Values of K and C (Fig. 3) for use in the above equation can be determined experimentally or estimated from published data.[1a,19]

The mathematical model assumes:

(1) one-dimensional heat and water flow;
(2) temperature of water and grains equal at a given depth;
(3) grain skeleton is incompressible;
(4) no air in pores;
(5) low velocity of water flow;
(6) ice formation takes place only at the freezing front;
(7) no water flow in the frozen zone;
(8) uniform (i.e. non-stratified material);
(9) constant suction at the ice front, sufficient to permit penetration.

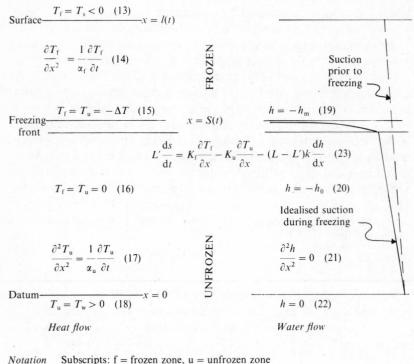

Surface —— $T_f = T_s < 0$ (13) —— $x = l(t)$

$$\frac{\partial T_f}{\partial x^2} = \frac{1}{\alpha_f} \frac{\partial T_f}{\partial t} \quad (14)$$

FROZEN

Suction prior to freezing

Freezing front —— $T_f = T_u = -\Delta T$ (15) —— $x = S(t)$

$h = -h_m$ (19)

$$L' \frac{ds}{dt} = K_f \frac{\partial T_f}{\partial x} - K_u \frac{\partial T_u}{\partial x} - (L - L')k \frac{dh}{dx} \quad (23)$$

$T_f = T_u = 0$ (16)

$h = -h_0$ (20)

Idealised suction during freezing

$$\frac{\partial^2 T_u}{\partial x^2} = \frac{1}{\alpha_u} \frac{\partial T_u}{\partial t} \quad (17)$$

UNFROZEN

$$\frac{\partial^2 h}{\partial x^2} = 0 \quad (21)$$

Datum —— $x = 0$
$T_u = T_w > 0$ (18)

$h = 0$ (22)

Heat flow   *Water flow*

Notation   Subscripts: f = frozen zone, u = unfrozen zone
T = temperature (°C)
t = time (s)
K = thermal conductivity (W m^{-1} °C^{-1})
L = latent heat of water (J kg^{-1})
L' = latent heat of soil (J kg^{-1})
α = thermal diffusivity (m^2 s^{-1}) = K/C
C = Volumetric heat capacity (J m^{-3} °C^{-1})
k = Darcy coefficient of permeability (m s^{-1})
h = excess suction head (m)
h_m = maximum value of h (m)
h_0 = value of h at bottom of freezing front (m)

FIG. 3.   Mathematical model of frost heave.

Simplified versions of this model, in which the mass transport term was ignored were used in developing the Stefan and modified Berggren formulae which relate the depth of frost penetration to the freezing index, expressed in degree days.[20] Finite difference techniques using an expanding mesh in the frozen zone and a contracting mesh in the unfrozen zone have been used to solve the equations associated with the model.

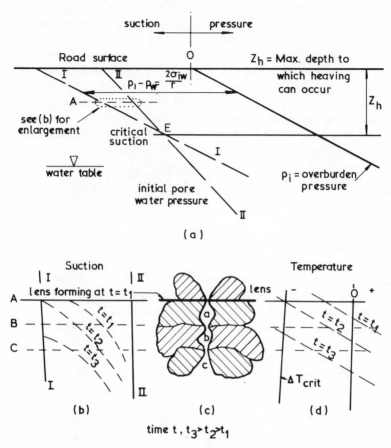

FIG. 4. Frost penetration and ice lensing. (a) Effect of depth to water table and overburden pressure (after Williams[9]); (b) enlarged view of variation of suction with time; (c) pore structure; (d) temperature variations corresponding to (b).

Predictions of rate of penetration of the zero isotherm which are in good agreement with experimental observations have been made with the water flow governed by eqns. (20) and (21).[2a,20–22,23a] Heave predictions are sensitive to the value assigned to h_0. It will be shown in the next section that the assumption of a constant value for h_0 is of limited validity.

The Effects of Fluctuations of Heat Flow and Suction

Figure 4(a) shows the variation of ice and water pressure with depth. The ice pressure, equal to the overburden pressure, increases with depth at roughly twice the rate of the initial hydrostatic pressure. For frost penetration, the pore water pressure must fall to the values given by the line I–I, eqn. (5), which is parallel to the P_i line. Ice penetration can occur without excess suction at depths greater than Z_h which is therefore the limiting depth to which heaving can occur.[9]

If a pressure is applied to the surface, the P_i line and therefore I–I is displaced to the right. Alternatively, if the water table is lowered by drainage the hydrostatic line II–II is displaced to the left. In both cases the intersection point E moves upwards and Z_h is reduced.

Suppose at the instant $t = t_1$ the freezing front had reached level A (Figs. 4(a) and (b)); the enlarged views (Figs. 4(b), (c) and (d)) are drawn to a common depth scale, and the throat diameters at levels A, B and C are assumed to be the same. At $t = t_1$, since P_w is greater than the critical value, ice cannot penetrate below level A and a lens will form with the temperature higher than that required to achieve critical curvature.

At $t = t_2$, both the temperature T (°C) and P_w have fallen to the critical value enabling ice to penetrate into pore 'a'. Once through the throat, ice can spread through the pore even if P_w is greater than the critical value. Water is still being drawn towards the freezing front.

At $t = t_3$, at level B, the critical conditions for penetration have been satisfied ($T < \Delta T$, $P_w < P_w$crit) and the ice will have penetrated into void 'b'. A lens will form if the ice reaches level C before the temperature drops to the critical value.

The capillary model thus provides an explanation of the frequently observed phenomenon of ice banding.[24]

Conduction is considered the most significant mechanism of heat flow.[1a] The variations in the components of heat flow are shown in Fig. 5. The 'penetration' section of Fig. 5(c) shows the instantaneous flows associated with Fig. 3.

For steady boundary temperatures, the zero isotherm will eventually reach its maximum depth. Ice penetration will cease at a slightly higher level when the temperature is no longer low enough to sustain the critical radius. A terminal lens will grow, reducing the thermal gradient and hence q_E. The radius of curvature will increase and the suction fall steadily. The zero isotherm will rise and any ice in large pores below the terminal lens will tend to melt.

The mathematical model of the previous section is being developed to include the lens growth phases. The increase in heaving rate with penetration rate[26] and the fact that 60–70 % of the heave in a modified TRRL test is attributed to the terminal lens[12] emphasises the importance

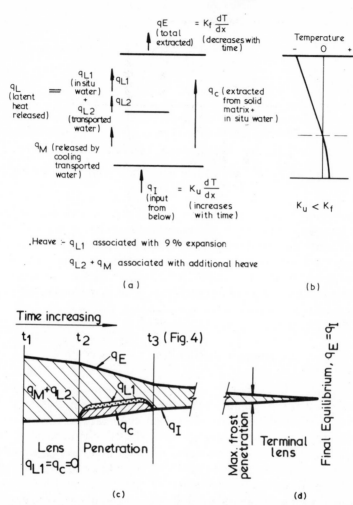

FIG. 5. Heat flow during frost heave. (a) Components (after Penner[25]); (b) temperature gradient; (c) with rhythmic banding; (d) approach to final equilibrium.

of this aspect. From the onset of freezing, rapid penetration of the zero isotherm maintains a high suction, with small fluctuations (Fig. 6) which favours ice penetration accompanied by a high heaving rate. Lensing during penetration of the zero isotherm will be negligible and the assumption of the constant suction, consistent with ice penetration, is reasonable for this phase.

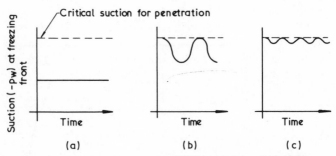

FIG. 6.   Fluctuation of suction with rate of penetration of zero isotherm. (a) Zero;
(b) moderate; (c) fast rate.

On the other hand, moderate rates of zero isotherm penetration will tend to be accompanied by greater fluctuations of suction (Fig. 6(b)) which will favour ice banding. Mathematical models for this condition must therefore consider the fluctuations of suction within the freezing front at least to the extent of estimating the equivalent constant suction. Mathematical modelling of the final phase of the terminal lens growth is simplified since the possibility of ice penetration is excluded.

DIRECT FROST HEAVE TESTS

Direct tests simulate road freezing conditions in the laboratory by subjecting cylinders of compacted material to freezing temperatures at their upper surfaces whilst their bases are held in contact with free water. A constant top temperature is applied in the TRRL test[6] in contrast to the USA CRREL test[27] in which temperature is adjusted to give a constant rate of zero isotherm penetration. In the CRREL test, classification is based on rate of heaving. Comparative tests on four pulverised fuel ashes of widely differing frost susceptibilities have indicated that similar classifications are obtained from the two tests.[28] Heaving pressure measurements have also been used as measure of frost susceptibility.[1b] However, the TRRL test is simpler and probably more realistic. Self-refrigerated units (SRUs) are likely to supersede cold rooms as the preferred testing facility in future specifications.

TRRL Test (Cold Room)
Compacted specimens, 102 mm diameter by 152 mm high, wrapped in waxed paper and supported on porous discs are placed with the discs

dipping into the water bath of a purpose-made insulated trolley. Up to nine specimens can be accommodated, the space between them being filled with coarse sand. The specimens are surmounted by tufnol discs containing locating dimples for vertical push rods which protrude through guide bars at the top of the trolley. The general arrangement, as adapted for SRUs is shown in Fig. 9.

After equilibrating for 24 h, the water level is topped up and the trolley pushed into the $-17°C$ cold room. The cold room temperature is maintained by a fan assisted cooler which defrosts automatically at regular intervals, typically 8 or 12 h. After initial cooling an internal heater maintains the water temperature at $+4°C$. Each day the water level is topped up, and the heave measured from the movement of the push rods. The final readings are taken at 250 h.

Specimens are compacted at or near optimum conditions and a minimum of three tested.[29,30] Additional tests are sometimes required if the results are scattered or if they fall close to a classification boundary.

On the basis of an empirical correlation based on the behaviour of subgrades in the 1940 and 1946–47 winters, materials were classified as:

(a) satisfactory (<13 mm);
(b) marginally frost susceptible (13–18 mm);
(c) very frost susceptible (>18 mm).

The test, developed as a research tool has been found to lack the reproducibility required for a compliance test.[31] Subsequent research has been concentrated on both the methods of specimen preparation and the permitted tolerances in the testing regime as sources of variability.

Theoretical considerations and experimental observations indicate the importance of maintaining steady boundary temperatures if reproducible results are to be obtained. Measurements have shown that variations of water temperature immediately beneath the porous discs are often well in excess of the controller tolerance ($\pm0·5°C$)[23b,32,33] partly due to the lack of convection currents to aid mixing when the surface temperatures fall below $+4°C$. Heat was flowing both between the specimens and the coarse sand insulation and also around the standard top caps which are 3 mm smaller than the specimen diameter. Use of full diameter top caps, replacement of the sand by vermiculite, substitution of a mercury contact thermometer (tolerance $\pm0·1°C$) and the addition of a stirrer greatly improved the repeatability.[32] However, the heave increased most probably because intermittent thawing periods which interrupt terminal ice lens growth were much reduced. Thus heaves corresponding to the values previously

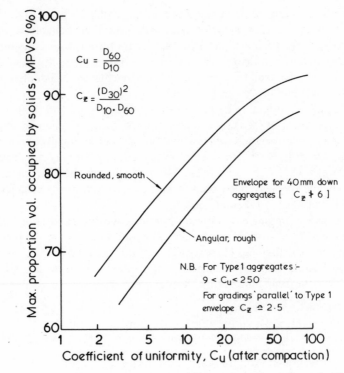

FIG. 7.   Relationship between compactability and grading (after refs. 36 and 37).

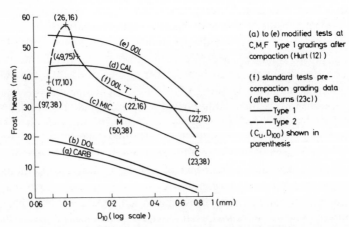

FIG. 8.   Effect of grading on heave of some limestones.

obtained after 250 h, were achieved in only 70 h in the modified test. The marked effect of defrost periods on heaving pressure development and by inference on terminal lens growth can best be avoided by switching to a chilled tank SRU.

Selection of Grading and Density for Test Specimens

Although sub-base and base materials may have a maximum particle size of 75 mm, the larger size fractions are excluded from many laboratory tests. Thus the typical maximum sizes permitted for the mould diameters given in parentheses are 20 mm (100 mm) and 37·5 or 40 mm (150 mm) for compaction tests and 50 mm (100 mm) for the TRRL test. Improved repeatability has been obtained in frost heave tests by restricting the maximum size of aggregate.[30,34] Scalping at 20 mm which may exclude nearly 40 % of the material, has been accompanied by an increase in heave which has made the results difficult to interpret.[34]

An alternative approach, currently under investigation, is to scalp at 37·5 mm, but increase the specimen diameter to 150 mm. Scalping at 37·5 instead of 50 mm, excludes only a small proportion (maximum 15 %), especially since most Type 1[4] sources supply 37·5 mm down material. The procedure has the great advantage that compaction tests (in a California Bearing Ratio (CBR) mould) and frost heave tests can be carried out at the same grading.

Currently, the selection of density and moulding water content is based on the result of a BS Standard Compaction Test[35] using the 2·5 kg rammer on 20 mm down material but adjustments are permitted to achieve a stable sample. Type 2 material has to be laid at the optimum moisture content determined by the BS vibrating hammer test[4] and a change to this test or its modified version MVHT[36] (modified vibrating hammer test) as a basis for frost heave testing is being considered.[34]

For gradings with a coefficient of curvature not greater than 6, compactibility, expressed as the maximum proportion of volume of solids, increases with the coefficient of uniformity C_u after compaction (Fig. 7).[36,37] Thus for a given maximum size of aggregate compacted under optimum conditions the resulting pore size distribution becomes much finer with increasing C_u.

The influence of grading on the frost heave of six limestones, compacted at optimum, is shown in Fig. 8. DOL, MIC and CAL are Magnesian Limestones with saturation moisture contents (SMCs) of 4·2, 13·9 and 4·6 % respectively. OOL is a Corallian Oolitic Limestone with an SMC of 5·4 %. OOL 'T' was obtained earlier from the same source. CARB is a

Carboniferous Limestone which is virtually non-porous (SMC of 0·5 %). OOL 'T' was tested at a range of gradings covering the entire Type 1 and 2 envelopes. The remainder were tested at Coarse, Mid and Fine (C: M: F). Type 1 gradings for 38 mm down material.[12]

The revised interim specification for frost heave testing of granular materials[34] recommends that the initial grading be representative of the source. Other workers[23d] advocate that since the 'as compacted' grading of the specimen governs its frost susceptibility, the initial grading should be adjusted so that the compacted specimen will have the same grading as in the road. This is a matter of some controversy. The number of gradings which have to be reported vary from nil to the four required by some County Engineers.[38] The author believes that at least one grading should be recorded, since it is an essential part of the sample description.

Degradation is limited almost entirely to the compaction stage. In vibrating hammer tests, a highly significant correlation is found between degradation expressed as the average change in percentage passing and both aggregate impact value and 10 % fines.[39] There is some evidence that the degradation in the field is much less than in the laboratory.[23d]

A difficulty in sample preparation and also in assessing initial gradings and degradation is that the size of the specimen is less than is required for a representative sample. Recombining individual weighed out single-sized fractions, the so-called 'graded grains' technique of preparing specimens, can be helpful.

Cohesive materials are compacted at 5 % air voids at their natural moisture contents, or if this is not known at 2 % above their plastic limit.[6]

Compaction of Specimens
The required amount of dry material and water for each individual specimen is thoroughly mixed and if necessary allowed to temper overnight. The mixed material is then placed into a tapered mould which is closed at one end with a protruding end plug. During this stage the material is lightly compacted in 3 layers with a 1·16 kg tamper. The upper end plug is inserted and should protrude by a similar amount to the lower one. The end plugs are then driven home at 50 mm min^{-1} in a compression machine capable of applying a maximum load of 400 kN.[34] This procedure differs from that originally adopted, in which pre-compaction was achieved with a wooden rammer and the maximum static load applied was 300 kN.[6]

Methods of reducing the static stage of the compaction and the accompanying degradation have been developed. Pre-compaction in 4 layers, each subjected to 2 to 3 s with a vibrating hammer, reduced the static load needed to less than 10 kN. Degradation was negligible except with a very soft limestone. For this, reduced degradation was achieved by placing the specimen in the mould with both end plugs in position and compacting it on a vibrating table for 2 min. During this process it was inverted several times to avoid both density gradients and migration of fines and water.[12]

Vibration techniques are particularly advantageous for the 150 mm diameter specimens now being considered since the reduction in the static load requirement allows the use of lighter moulds.

Self-refrigerated Units

Development of SRUs as cheaper and more convenient alternatives to the cold room commenced with the adaptation of commercial chilled tank deep freezes.[40] An early design which may well merit further consideration and development had chiller coils arranged at the top of the tank, giving a potentially better air temperature distribution. This unit was operated in a +4 °C room thus simplifying control of the water temperature but losing the flexibility of operating the SRU in any ambient temperature.[15]

Comparative tests between a conventional chilled tank and cold room showed an excellent agreement for the most important heave range (i.e. <20 mm) and led to the development of a commercially available unit.[30] Elsewhere, a forced air unit was developed and marketed.[41]

Subsequently other investigators and manufacturers have modified and developed units of both the basic types which are illustrated in Fig. 9. The water tank dimensions and specimen support arrangements are very similar to those of the original TRRL trolleys. A pump which may be submersible or external, circulates water through a sparge pipe. An auxiliary water cooler can be incorporated into the circuit if required. A mercury contact thermometer or thermistor feedback controls the heater which maintains a constant water temperature.

In the forced air unit, cold air at a thermostatically controlled temperature is circulated by a fan assisted unit cooler. Although a moisture absorption core reduces the problem, defrosting is necessary at regular intervals. The introduction of baffles can improve markedly the distribution of temperature above the nine samples.[23b] Greater uniformity of the top of specimen temperatures has been achieved by replacing the normal top discs with highly conductive ones, consisting of metal plates with vertical fins attached.[42].

In the chilled tank unit (Fig. 9(b)), direct cooling of the water can be obtained either by operating the by-pass valves to activate the refrigerating coils beneath the tank or alternatively, the auxiliary cooler may be used.

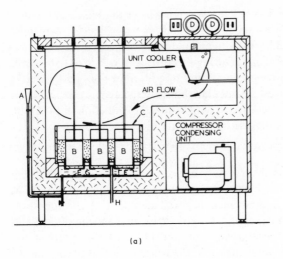

(a)

A   Water filler + level indicator
B   Specimen
C   Removable box
D   Temperature indicator/control
E   Water pump
F   Sparge pipe
G   Heater
H   Overflow
J   Refrigerating coils
K   By-pass valves
L   Fan
M   Mariotte vessel
N   Chart recorder
P   Lid catch

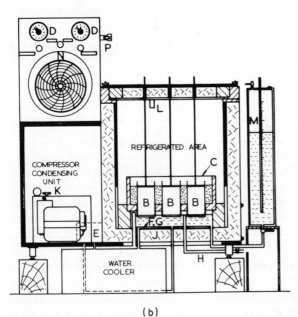

(b)

FIG. 9. Self-refrigerating units. (a) Forced air; (b) chilled tank.

Whilst the former method may be sufficient for commercial tests, the independent control of water temperature given by the second system is preferred for research. The water level is automatically regulated by a Mariotte vessel. Spatial variations and fluctuations of temperature, immediately beneath the porous stones, of less than $\pm 0.35\,°C$ appear possible with this system. A mercury capillary controller maintains the air temperature at $-17\,°C \pm 1\,°C$ and another provides failsafe water heating in the event of the primary feedback device failing. No defrosting is needed during the 250 h test. A small fan has recently been added, to circulate the air.

An integral chart recorder provides continuous traces of air and water temperatures during the tests. Later models now commercially available, include a digital read out and selector units for use with thermocouples which monitor the temperature distribution within the specimens. Provision is also being made for the auxiliary water cooler, if required, to be mounted internally.

In specifying SRUs, use should be made of existing test methods whenever possible.[43]

Precise Freezing Cells

More precise control can be obtained from individually controlled cooling plates than from cold air circulating above the specimens. Plates can be cooled by circulating refrigerant or by thermoelectric (Peltier) devices in which a temperature differential is created by passing a current through a junction of dissimilar materials.[44] A typical Peltier battery extracts heat from a cold face whilst the heat is removed from the opposite (hot) face by the circulation of cooling water.

Although Peltier devices have been criticised on the grounds of cost, possible uneven temperature distribution, and their indeterminate life,[45] they have the great advantage of precise control and versatility. Used in a $+4\,°C$ space, a 19 W battery is sufficiently powerful to perform a TRRL type test, although a greater capacity may be needed in ambient temperatures. The battery is mounted on a copper plate (Fig. 10) which incorporates a thermistor feedback controller capable of regulating the temperature to within $\pm 0.1\,°C$. The sample is supported and insulated exactly as in the standard test. Both the level and temperature of the water is closely controlled. A guard ring through which antifreeze is circulated maintains the top of the insulation at constant temperature although not within such close tolerances as the Peltier unit.

The controller has the facility not only for maintaining constant

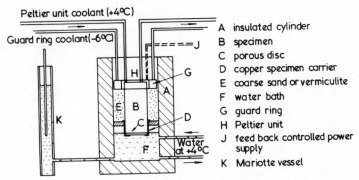

FIG. 10.   Precise freezing cell.

temperatures but also for cycling them between limits to simulate diurnal temperature variations. A thermo-electric guard ring is available for use with cycling tests.

So far the heaves achieved have been much less than with standard tests, due most probably to differing penetration rates and boundary conditions. The more rapid penetration gives a higher heaving rate but for a shorter time thus giving a lower final heave. Also in this system the constant temperature is applied to the moving top of the specimen whereas in the normal TRRL test, the heaving specimen protrudes into the cold air so that the sides are subjected to direct cooling. The precise unit, more closely achieving uni-directional conditions, will tend to yield a smaller terminal lens than the standard apparatus.[23e]

The contribution of the within particle pores to heave can be obtained from a precise freezing cell test in which the specimen is a rock core which has been cut through horizontally. By locating the feedback device in the cut the zero isotherm should be maintained at that level and an ice lens grown.

Verification of Testing Facilities

A final check of the proper functioning of the apparatus and correctness of technique using either comparative testing or a standard material is highly desirable. Ideally, for this purpose a natural or artificial material is required which:

(1)   has physical properties within the range normally encountered in frost heave testing;

(2)   is closely specified, particularly with respect to grading;

(3)   will be readily available to the same specification for the foreseeable future.

The alternatives seem to be either stockpiling a suitable graded natural material or using a material prepared for industrial processing.

Effect of an Improved Test Specification on the Classification Limits
With a non-fluctuating temperature regime, heave is likely to increase so that the limits will require re-definition. It would be better to shorten the test at this stage, since the scatter tends to increase with heave not least because of direct cooling from the sides of high heave specimens. Not only is this in contrast with the road situation but it also magnifies the differences between testing units. Even with the apparatus as originally specified, satisfactory classification could be obtained with a shortened test.[15,28,32,46]

INDIRECT ASSESSMENT OF FROST SUSCEPTIBILITY

Indirect methods may be based on soil or aggregate classification tests[6,47] which will probably have been undertaken for other purposes or, alternatively on special tests, e.g. suction characteristics.

Methods Based on Classification Tests
Clays with a plasticity index greater than 15 (if well drained) or 20 (when the water table is within 600 mm of the foundation) are considered non-frost susceptible.[6] For non-porous granular materials, many criteria based on grading have been advanced [48] often in the form of an upper limit on the amount of fines present. For porous materials in which the within particle pores make a significant contribution, the saturation moisture content (SMC) has been used as an index property. The SMC is best determined by evacuating the specimens, covering them with de-aired water and allowing them to stand for 24 h under vacuum. Individual results can be quite scattered (Fig. 11) suggesting that a large number of individual specimens should be tested to obtain a reliable average.

Such methods give only general guidance and have been found to lack reliability, largely due to their failure to reflect the critical factors in the frost heave process, e.g. SMC considers only total open porosity whereas it is the size of the pores which is critical.

Suction Characteristics
Suction characteristics not only enable pore size characteristics to be inferred but have direct application in estimating freezing point depression, unfrozen water content, unsaturated permeability, and air (or ice) entry

values. Alternative methods of estimating pore size distribution from optical or electron photomicrographs are tedious and involve expensive apparatus. Moreover it is the critical pore entrance diameter which is inferred from the suction characteristic rather than some intermediate value, between the throat and occupation diameters, that is obtained from photomicrographs of a section.

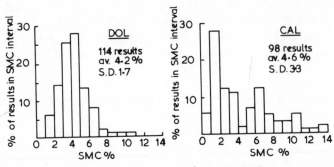

FIG. 11.   Saturation moisture contents.

Soil suction characteristics are measured by standard techniques appropriate to the suction range, e.g. capillary rise or suction plate (pF < 2·8), pressure membrane (pF < 4 or 5), vapour pressure (pF > 5).[49] For subgrade soils, criteria based on pore size distribution show no better correlation with field performance than those based on particle size distribution.[1c] However, in many cases the maximum suction used, pF 2·5 or lower, was less than may be appropriate to the frost heave process. For frost susceptibility studies on sub-base materials both overall aggregate suction characteristics (ASCs) on 100 mm diameter specimens and individual rock particle suction characteristics (RSCs) are required up to pF 4. The pressure membrane technique suffers from long equilibrium times and poor membrane reliability but a relatively new osmotic method gives results in three to five days.[12,23f]

In the osmotic technique, the specimens are separated by two dialysis membranes from a solution of polyethylene glycol (carbowax 6000) (Fig. 12) which is kept at a constant temperature. Few of the large carbowax molecules are able to pass through the membrane which is, however, permeable to the porewater and its much smaller dissolved ions. The osmotic pressure of the carbowax solution which varies with concentration (Fig. 12(b)) is therefore an equivalent matrix suction.

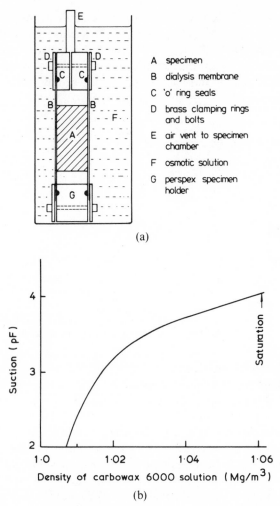

A specimen

B dialysis membrane

C 'o' ring seals

D brass clamping rings
   and bolts

E air vent to specimen
   chamber

F osmotic solution

G perspex specimen
   holder

(a)

(b)

FIG. 12.   Osmotic suction apparatus. (a) Cell; (b) osmotic suction vs. density of
typical carbowax 6000 solution.

The cell shown can accommodate up to six 10 mm thick slabs of rock
obtained from individual particles or alternatively a disc of compacted
aggregate sliced from a specimen prepared as for the standard frost heave
test.

Individual results on rock slabs, expressed as the degree of saturation
with respect to the SMC, are generally quite scattered, so that a large

number of results are required to obtain an accurate average. The scatter from aggregate specimens is less, due to the averaging effect of a large number of particles. Although in theory, the between particle pore distribution can be obtained by subtraction, the accuracy of this process is limited both by scatter and the assumptions involved.

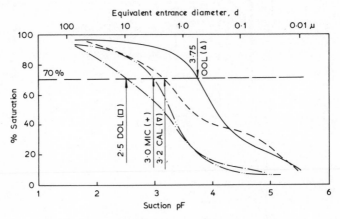

FIG. 13.   Rock suction characteristics—desorption.

The heave results obtained on the Type 1 aggregates (Fig. 8) support the hypothesis that the total heave is derived from the sum of 'between particle' and 'within particle' pore effects.[12,13] Thus for a given grading, frost susceptibility should be ranked by a characteristic 'within particle' pore size or its equivalent suction (Fig. 13). Heaving pressure results suggested that pF_{70}, the suction corresponding to 70% saturation was an appropriate characteristic. Figure 14 shows that for the materials and gradings used, frost susceptibility increases with pF_{70} of the rock. Whilst further testing is needed to confirm the general applicability of the results, they suggest that limestones for which pF_{70} exceeds 2·5 should be considered frost susceptible.

Permeability Considerations

Whilst the permeability of the material both unfrozen and in its partially frozen state in the freezing front is a major constraint on frost heave, it has to be considered in relation to the suction. An idealised relationship between permeability and suction is shown in Fig. 15. Once the suction exceeds the bubbling pressure, the permeability falls rapidly as the amount

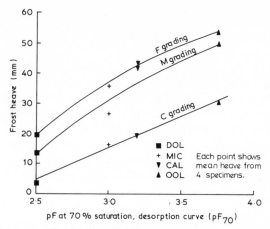

FIG. 14.   Heave vs. pF_{70} for four limestone aggregates compacted at maximum dry density.

of water left in the pores decreases. The measurement of unsaturated permeability requires special apparatus but estimates can be made from the saturated permeability and suction characteristics.[15,50] The product of the saturated permeability and the bubbling pressure has, in essence, been proposed as a characteristic of frost susceptibility for soils.[51] However, a number of the simplifying assumptions inherent in the proposal are open to question.[1b] Furthermore for porous limestones, the within aggregate pores which are likely to be primarily responsible for the permeability at the top of the freezing front may be supplied with water from the underlying between aggregate pores. Suction permeability characteristics are being studied relative to the mathematical model and it is perhaps in this context, more than as a simple criterion that their future application lies.

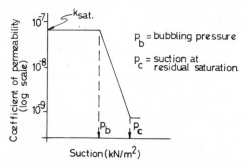

FIG. 15.   Permeability vs. suction (idealised).

EFFECT OF MATERIAL AND ENVIRONMENT ON ACTUAL FROST HEAVE

The influence of the intrinsic properties of sub-base aggregates has been discussed earlier. For other materials, e.g. clay subgrades, other intrinsic properties such as mineralogy or surface activity may be dominant. Even if the intrinsic properties are unfavourable it may be possible to specify a mode of usage (grading, stabilisation, etc.) which will enable the material to be accommodated in a given situation. Alternatively or additionally, its use may be restricted to favourable environments with either a mild climate or more likely, with little or no access to underground water.

Mode of Material Usage
For unstabilised granular materials, the actual heave is influenced by the interrelated factors of density and grading. A change giving a reduction in pore size will produce greater or less heave depending on whether the original size was above or below the optimum for heave.

For the Type 1 limestones, curves (a) to (e) in Fig. 8, at any given grading, density had little effect on the heave. Lowering the density appeared to introduce a few large voids, leaving a constant matrix of finer pores, independent of density. This matrix appeared to control the heave. In other tests, a decrease in heave accompanied an increase in density of silty clay soil.[6]

Although there may be practical difficulties, not least with degradation, the evidence suggests that doubtful materials should be placed to give the coarsest possible gradings after compaction.

It may also be possible to reduce the quantity of imported non-frost susceptible material when a local frost susceptible source is available, by mixing the two materials. Results of laboratory tests in which various proportions of high and low heave limestones were mixed are shown in Fig. 16. For these particular aggregates, substitution of low heave fines reduced the heave of the highly frost susceptible material more than did the substitution of an equal volume of low heave coarse. This may not be generally true and it would be essential to test specific materials before deciding to adopt this technique in practice. Overseas, a number of special methods have been used to give protection against frost heave damage.[1e] These include inserting an insulated layer to prevent the penetration of the zero isotherm. Alternatively, a water barrier can be incorporated. An ingenious application of this principle is the use of a coarse gravel layer sandwiched between protective fabric membranes.[52]

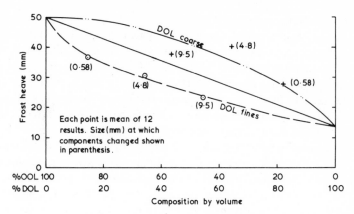

FIG. 16. Heave of mixed specimens.

Finally, materials can be stabilised by additives. Both pulverised fuel ash[53] and colliery shales[54,55] have been stabilised successfully with cement which gives tensile strength and often reduces permeability. Although the curing period between the making and testing of specimens is not specified, 7 days have been found satisfactory. Compliance with the compressive strength requirement for cement stabilised materials (see ref. 61) has rendered some materials, notably stabilised chalk, frost resistant.[56] However, in a recent study[55] of cement stabilised colliery shales, the most discriminating parameter of frost resistance was found to be tensile strength, since the material must fracture before significant heave can take place. Thus, if the tensile strength exceeds the heaving pressure (which may increase with stabilisation if the critical pore size is reduced) frost heave damage is prevented. Frost shattering, perhaps by a mechanism involving positive pore pressures[57] is, however, still a possibility. A test in which the specimens are subjected to several freezing cycles may be needed in these circumstances. Pending further research, care should be exercised, particularly if consideration is being given to stabilising untried materials to form road bases.

Both lime stabilisation of heavy clays to improve their strength and the addition of low amounts of cement to highly cohesive colliery shales can increase their frost susceptibility, presumably due to the clay colloids aggregating, thus facilitating water transport. In contrast, where additives reduce permeability, e.g. bentonite or sodium tripolyphosphate with chalk[6] or cement with pulverised fuel ash,[53] this factor is significant in reducing heave.

Climatic Factors

On average, severe winters, i.e. those having 40 or more days of consecutive frost, occur nationwide in Britain at infrequent intervals.[34] The corresponding freezing index is about 150 °C days which is about a tenth of that commonly experienced in North America. In 3 days, frost penetration of 300 mm has been observed, rising to 375 mm in 10 days. Although isolated frost penetration of up to 530 mm has been observed[3] current design is based on a value of 450 mm.

A slow rate of penetration favours lens growth and high heave. This effect has been observed in a test pit[23g,58] and may also explain the continental observation that 'mild' winters produce greater frost heave than 'severe' ones.[1d,1f] Heave in mild winters may also be aggravated by temperature fluctuations which favour the growth of intermediate lenses rather than ice penetration.

Position of Water Table

The effect of varying the depth to the water table has been investigated in two series of experiments in a pit, 1·5 m deep, conducted by TRRL. In the first[59] the surfacing and base courses were asphalt blocks, 100 mm thick and 300 mm square, laid on a 200 mm sub-base of compacted limestone wet mix which was not frost susceptible. The subgrade consisted of 900 mm of brick earth (silty clay, LL = 30, PL = 19, PI = 11, frost heave 19 to 23 mm depending on density) compacted in 150 mm layers. A series of vertical 100 mm diameter gravel drains at 300 mm centres, connecting to a horizontal gravel blanket maintained the water level at chosen values ranging from 0·3 to 1·2 m below the bottom of the sub-base.

By lowering the top temperature to −17 °C, zero isotherm penetrations of approximately $\frac{2}{3}$ m were achieved. Except at the lowest water table level, CBR values were temporarily reduced by factors of 2 to 3 after thawing. Frost heave increased considerably when the water table was raised from 0·6 to 0·3 m below the sub-base. It was concluded that for clays having liquid limits not less than 30, heave and thaw weakening were significant only when the water table was within 600 mm of the sub-base. However, for chalks, field evidence indicated that the heave was independent of depth to water table within the range 150 to 600 mm.[60]

In a second series of tests with a similar system, 3 layers of asphalt blocks overlay 300 mm of compacted limestone sub-base. The sub-base material in this case was frost susceptible with a heave of 38 mm in the standard test. The subgrade was a non frost susceptible sandy gravel. The results of 21 test runs confirmed that although there was considerable scatter, the heave reduced as the depth to the water table increased.[23g,58]

Neither of these experiments was directly concerned with the effect of permeability of the subgrade on the heave. However, when an attempt to use silty clay apparently similar to that used previously was made in the second series of tests, it proved to be practically impermeable and no heave occurred.[23g] Similarly, when composite specimens made with frost susceptible materials in which the bottom 50 mm were replaced by London Clay, the frost heave was reduced to negligible proportions.[6] Thus, even if the water table is constant, identical road pavements subject to the same freezing conditions would be expected to heave by different amounts depending on the subgrade properties. Conversely, it may be safe to use relatively susceptible materials when the subgrade is impermeable.

DESIGN AGAINST FROST HEAVE DAMAGE

The Nature of Rational Design
Accepting that 'total' heave under field conditions is a suitable characteristic, a limiting value must be assigned to it so that unacceptable heave and damage is prevented. The factors which affect the heave must be quantified and processed to produce an estimate of the actual damage parameter. By comparing this with the limiting value, the design, or more particularly the material, is either accepted or rejected.

The input variables requiring quantification are:

(1) material (intrinsic properties and mode of usage);
(2) climate (depth of frost penetration);
(3) availability of water (depth to water table; permeability and capillarity of the subgrade).

There is a strong interaction between the way in which the variables are quantified and the method of analysis. The basis of the analysis can be, in order of increasing confidence:

(a) empirical correlation;
(b) qualitative model;
(c) quantitative model;

The quantitative model will subsume the earlier stages. Furthermore, since the proposed model needs checking against the performance of materials both in standard test conditions and in field or pit trials, its development stimulates research into the assessment of material properties by both direct and indirect tests.

Further Work Required

Research in progress should produce a revised comprehensive specification for the TRRL test, to supersede the interim version.

Development of the quantitative model may permit the use of indirect assessments of frost heave, based for example on the RSC determined by the osmotic technique. Whilst this involves simpler and lighter apparatus, the test duration and operator involvement may not be much different from that of a shortened direct test.

Data is needed on the limiting value of heave to prevent damage to a modern road and how this relates to the performance of the material in direct and/or indirect tests. A hard winter would provide some data, but well maintained roads constructed to existing specifications should not fail. Nevertheless, observations might justify extending the Scottish criteria to the whole of the UK. For further progress, trial sections built to lower specifications, so that some failures occur, are desirable to demonstrate that any chosen limit is not over-conservative.

Finally, data on the effect of the subgrade permeability and capillarity on the supply of water to the freezing front are required for a wide range of subgrades and water table depths. Tests on multi-layer compacted cylinders are preferable, at least initially, to pit experiments for this purpose. The extension of the quantitative model from a single layer to a multi-layer system should be straightforward.

The Revised Procedure in Practice

The simplest procedure would be to vary the acceptable limit of heave in the TRRL test in accordance with the site conditions. Thus a series of charts or tables would be prepared relating the limits to the depth of water table and the equivalent permeability of the subgrade. These could be extended to include different depths of frost penetration if required. Density, grading and stabilisation effects would normally be taken into account by testing the material in an appropriate condition. However, it should not be impossible to apply a correction factor when the test has been done at a standard condition.

Use of such charts would achieve a rational and economic design. Routine design would remain a simple procedure but the data and the quantitative model used in the development of the charts would be available to assist in interpretation, should any unusual circumstances arise. For many cases, it is probable that the limits would be sufficiently high to reduce substantially the amount of testing required. Greater use would be made of locally available materials, and the unnecessary use of high quality materials avoided.

REFERENCES

1. (a) JOHANSEN, Ø. p. 49–50 (1, 165–8); (b) OBERMEIER, S. F., p. 68–9 (1, 251–60); (c) GASKIN, P. N. and RAYMOND, G. P., p. 76–8 (1, 295–309); (d) KEUBLER, G., p. 37–9 (1, 133–40); (e) Section V, p. 177–214 (2, 243–450); (f) Discussion, p. 41–2. Proc. OECD symposium on frost action in roads 1973. (Summaries only in proceedings. Full text in reports volumes referred to in parentheses.)
2. (a) AGUIRRE-PUENTE, J., FREMOND, M. and MENOT, J. M., p. 5–22 (in French); (b) WILLIAMS, P. J., p. 42–53. Proc. Int. symposium on frost action in soils, Univ. of Lulea, Sweden, 1977.
3. CRONEY, D. RRL Lab. Note LN 459DC, 19 p. (unpublished), 1963.
4. DEPARTMENT OF TRANSPORT. Specification for road and bridge works, HMSO, London, 1976.
5. SCOTTISH DEVELOPMENT DEPT., Tech. memo. SH7/72, 1 p., 1972.
6. CRONEY, D. and JACOBS, J. C. RRL Report LR 90, 68 p., Crowthorne, 1967.
7. PENNER, E. Proc. 1st Int. conf. on permafrost, 197–202, 1963.
8. EVERETT, D. H. and HAYNES, J. M. *RILEM Bull.*, 31–8, June, 1965.
9. WILLIAMS, P. J. Norw. Geotech. Inst., Publication No. 72, 1967.
10. KOOPMANS, R. W. R. and MILLER, R. D. *Soil Sci. Soc. America*, **30**, 680–5, 1966.
11. SCHOFIELD, R. K. Proc. 3rd Int. conf. soil sci., 2, 38–48, 1935.
12. HURT, K. G. 'The prediction of the frost susceptibility of limestone aggregates with reference to road construction', Ph.D. thesis, Univ. of Nottingham, 1976.
13. NICHOLLS, R. A. 'Frost heave of limestones', M.Phil. thesis, Univ. of Nottingham, 1970.
14. SUTHERLAND, H. B. and GASKIN, P. N. Proc. 2nd Int. conf. on permafrost, 409–19, 1973.
15. ONALP, A. 'The mechanism of frost heave in soils with particular reference to chemical stabilisation', Ph.D. thesis, Univ. of Newcastle upon Tyne, 1970.
16. MILLER, R. D. Hwy Res. Rec. 393, 1–11, 1972.
17. RUCKLI, R. Proc. 2nd Int. conf. soil mech. and found. eng., **2**, 282–7, 1948.
18. GOLD, L. W. Hwy Res. Bull. 168, 65–73, 1957.
19. KERSTEN, M. S. Hwy Res. Brd., Special Report No. 2, 1951.
20. ALDRICH, H. P. Hwy Res. Bull. 135, 124–48, 1956.
21. AGUIRRE-PUENTE, J. and FREMOND, M. Proc. 2nd conf. on soil water problems in cold regions, Alberta, Canada, 1976.
22. CANARD, L., DUPAS, A., FREMOND, M. and LEVY, M. Proc. VII Int. cong. Les problemes poses par la gelification, Le Havre (in French), 1975.

23. (a) HOLDEN, J. T., p. 87–93; (b) HILL, J., p. 23–7; (c) BURNS, J., p. 72–4; (d) HILL, J., p. 59–64; (e) DUDEK, S., p. 13–21; (f) HURT, K. G., p. 133–8; (g) BURNS, J., p. 127–31, p. 139. Proc. coll. on frost heave testing and research, Dept. Civil Engineering, Univ. of Nottingham, 1977.

24. TABER, S. Public Roads, 11, 6, 113–32, 1930.

25. PENNER, E. ASTM Proceedings, 60, 1151–65, 1960.

*26. KAPLAR, C. W. Hwy Res. Rec. 304, 1–13, 1970.

27. HALEY, J. F. and KAPLAR, C. W. Hwy Res. Brd., Special Report No. 2, 553–7, 1952.

28. SUTHERLAND, H. B. and GASKIN, P. N. Canad. Geotech. J., 10, 3, 553–7, 1973.

29. JACOBS, J. C. RRL Lab. Note LN 766 JCJ, 16 (unpublished), 1965.

30. KETTLE, R. J. and WILLIAMS, R. I. T. RILEM Bull. Mats. Struc., 6, 34, 299–306, 1973.

31. RRL Road Research (Annual Report), 83, 1971.

* 32. JONES, R. H. and HURT, K. G. Hwy and Road Const., 43, 1787/8 (July/August), p. 8–13; 1791 (Nov.), p. 37 and 52; 1975.

33. TRRL. Unpublished work.

↣ * 34. TRRL Supplementary Report SR 318, 1977.

35. BS 1377. Methods of test for soils for civil engineering purposes; British Standards Institution, London, 1975.

●36. PIKE, D. C. and ACOTT, S. M. TRRL Supplementary Report SR 140 UC, 1975.

37. PIKE, D. C. Private communication, 1977.

38. County Surv. Soc. North Count. Soils and Mat. Eng. Gp. Specification to be applied in conjunction with LR 90, 1976 (unpublished).

39. PIKE, D. C. RRL Tech. Note TN 657, 1971 (unpublished).

40. NELLIST, G. R. J. Sci. Instrum., 44, 533–55, 1967.

◦41. ANON. Hwy and Traffic Engineering, 23–4, June, 1971.

42. DILMAGHANI, S. 'Freezing behaviour of compacted soil', Ph.D. thesis, Univ. of Birmingham, 1976.

43. BS 4864. Recommendations on the design and testing of enclosures for environmental testing, British Standards Institution, London, 1973.

44. LECHNER, W. Philips Tech. Rev., 27, 5, 113–30, 1966.

◦45. KAPLAR, C. W. Hwy Res. Rec. 215, 48–9, 1968.

46. KETTLE, R. J. and WILLIAMS, R. I. T. Canad. Geotech. J., 13, 2, 127–38, 1976.

●47. TRANSPORT AND ROAD RESEARCH LABORATORY. Road Note No. 29, HMSO, London, 1970.

48. TOWNSEND, D. L. and CSATHY, T. I. 'A compilation of frost susceptibility criteria', Queen's Univ., Ontario, 1961.

49. CRONEY, D. and COLEMAN, J. D. Proc. symp. pore pressure and suction in soils, 31–7, 1960.

50. LALIBERTE, G. E., BROOKS, R. H. and COREY, A. T. Proc. ASCE J. Irr. and Dr. Div., IR1 (March), p. 57–71, 1968.

51. WISSA, A. E. Z., MARTIN, R. T. and KOUTSOFTAS, D. Mass. Inst. Tech., 316, 1972.

52. ROTH, H. Int. conf. on use of fabrics in geotechnics, Paris, 1, 23–8, 1977.

●53. SUTHERLAND, H. B. and GASKIN, P. N. Canad. Geotech. J., 7, 1, 69–78, 1970.

54. KETTLE, R. J. and WILLIAMS, R. I. T. Materials and Structures, 19, 5, 99–107, 1976.

55. KETTLE, R. J. and WILLIAMS, R. I. T. TRB Record (in press).
56. SHERWOOD, P. and POCOCK, R. G. *Roads and Road Const.*, **47,** 554 (Feb.), 43–50, 1969.
57. BLACHERE, J. R. and YOUNG, J. E. *J. Testing and Evaluation*, **3,** 4, 273–7, 1975.
58. BURNS, J. TRRL Report SR 305, 1977.
59. JACOBS, J. C. and WEST, G. RRL Report LR 54, 1966.
60. CRONEY, D. Proc. symp. on chalk in earthworks and foundations, p. 111, 1965.
61. WILLIAMS, R. I. T. Cement stabilised materials, Chapter 5, in *Developments in Highway Pavement Engineering*—1, P. S. Pell (ed.), Applied Science Publishers, London, 1978.

Chapter 4

ASSESSMENT OF PERFORMANCE AND OVERLAY DESIGN OF FLEXIBLE PAVEMENTS†

N. W. LISTER

Transport and Road Research Laboratory, Crowthorne, UK

and

C. K. KENNEDY

Plymouth Polytechnic, UK

SUMMARY

The basic requirements of a system for strengthening roads are a rapid technique of measuring their structural condition and a design method for determining the timing and extent of the strengthening measures.

The two main types of equipment for the measurement of the structural condition of a road in terms of the deflection of its surface are described— those which employ some form of dynamic loading on a plate and those which utilise a rolling wheel load moving at creep speed.

The development of the Transport and Road Research Laboratory method for estimating the unexpired life of existing pavements and strengthening of roads with bituminous overlays is described, with emphasis being given to matching of overlay requirements to the varying structural conditions found along roads in need of strengthening. Case histories illustrating the validity of the method are presented. A description is also given of a different design approach, the Shell method, in which pavement conditions are analysed using multi-layer elastic theory applied to deflections measured by a falling-weight loading technique.

† Any views expressed in this chapter are not necessarily those of the Department of the Environment.

INTRODUCTION

Chapters 1–3 in the first book in the series indicate that pavement design procedures and the materials available are subject to continuing improvement. However, the great increase which has taken place in the last twenty-five years in both the weight of individual wheel loads and their number has led to difficulty in designing pavements for heavily trafficked roads for lives of longer than about twenty years using road materials presently available. It is also unlikely to be economic to attempt to design roads for lighter traffic to last for longer periods without requiring structural strengthening. Structural deterioration under traffic therefore takes place to some extent in all pavements although in those that are well designed its development is a very slow and generally seasonal process. As virtually all roads continue to carry traffic for much longer than their conventional design lives periodic strengthening of all roads, and not just those which are poorly designed or constructed, is inevitable.

Some idea of the importance of structural strengthening can be obtained by comparing the present rate of expenditure of about £170 million per annum on the pavement elements of new roads in the UK with the expenditure on structural strengthening of about £100 million per annum. Bearing in mind that many parts of the major arterial road network built during the last two decades are reaching, or will in the next few years reach, the end of their design lives, expenditure on this type of road may well increase.

The position is similar in most industrially developed countries, and it is therefore appropriate that increasing attention is now being paid worldwide to develop methods for the design of road strengthening measures. In the past, pavement strengthening has almost invariably been carried out because considerable damage, visible at the road surface, has taken place. Because a pavement thus damaged can contribute little structurally to a pavement strengthened by overlaying, the overlay thickness required is generally considerable. Alternatively, reconstruction of the roadbase and surfacing may be necessary. Such solutions are generally more expensive than if a thinner overlay is applied earlier, before major surface deterioration is apparent and before the structural integrity of the pavement is seriously impaired when the road is in a critical and not a failed condition.

A system for the design of structural strengthening measures must therefore have two basic elements:

    (a)   it should be able to predict the remaining life of a pavement under

traffic so that strengthening by overlaying can be timed to coincide
with the onset of critical conditions;
(b)   it should design the thickness of overlay required to prolong the life
of a road to carry any given traffic.

Roads will also require reconstruction rather than strengthening if they
are too badly damaged to be overlaid, level limitations preclude the use of
overlays, or reconstruction of the left-hand lane of a multi-lane highway is
more economic than overlaying all its lanes. Any comprehensive design
system should therefore include recommendations for reconstruction.

Essential to a design method is some measurement of the structural
condition of the road which is sufficiently rapid to allow long lengths of road
to be surveyed conveniently. The type of measurement and the frequency
with which it can be made influence the design method and its likely
accuracy. Methods of measurement are therefore covered first in the
chapter and are followed by a brief review of the main types of possible
design methods. The method of measurement and design developed for use
in the UK are then considered in more detail.

METHODS OF MEASUREMENT OF STRUCTURAL CONDITION

A characteristic feature of most roads is the considerable variation in
structural stiffness and strength along their length. This is demonstrated
both by measurements of pavement stiffness (possibly in terms of the
deflection of the road surface) and by the non-uniform way in which
pavement damage develops. The variation dictates the desired spacing of
measurements of structural strength. The necessary spacing of the
measurements will also depend on whether they are to be used only to divide
the road into lengths of similar strength, or to design the strengthening
measures themselves. Given the need to survey very considerable
kilometers of road each year, rapidity of measurement is essential if
adequately close spacing of measurements is to be achieved; the need for
speed of operation limits the possible techniques to those which operate on
the road surface.

Road roughness is relatively quick and easy to measure[1] and its periodic
measurement can give a general indication of pavement deterioration and
of the possible need to restore the riding quality of the road. However, only
in as far as the roughness is structurally associated, can the measurements

serve as an indicator of the need for structural strengthening. The measurements cannot in any case be used directly to characterise structural conditions in physical terms, or to design overlay thicknesses. For this purpose some measure related to the stress–strain response of the pavement is required.

The transient displacement or deflection of the road surface under an applied load represents the sum of all the vertical strains in the pavement and subgrade and can be expected to correlate in some broad sense with road strength and performance.

Although modelling of the dynamic behaviour of flexible pavements by simple layered elastic systems, as discussed by Peattie,[26] is known to be a simplification of their actual behaviour under load, such modelling is useful in giving some idea of the way in which deflection is influenced by the stiffness of the pavement and subgrade.

For a given pavement the deflection w can be related to the modulus E_1 of the pavement built on a subgrade of modulus E_2 by[2]

$$w \propto \frac{1}{(E_1)^{0.33}} \frac{1}{(E_2)^{0.67}} \tag{1}$$

Deflection, although responsive to changes in pavement stiffness is more sensitive to those in the subgrade.

The radius of curvature R of the road surface beneath the applied load is another possible measure of road behaviour. For pavements of reasonable thickness[3]

$$wR \propto \left(\frac{E_1}{E_2}\right)^{0.6} \tag{2}$$

Combining eqns. (1) and (2) indicates that the radius of curvature is highly sensitive to pavement stiffness and relatively unaffected by that of the subgrade.

In measuring road strength there is therefore some merit in supplementing deflection measurements which give a general indication of structural stiffness, with measurements of curvature relating more specifically to the pavement itself. Largely because it is relatively easy to measure, deflection has been widely used as an indicator of structural condition; radius of curvature, normally derived from measurements of deflection difference, inevitably presents greater problems of measurement and consequently has, until recently, been less frequently employed.

Rolling Wheel Techniques

In service the road is deflected under the action of the rolling wheel loads of lorry traffic and when deflection is measured for the assessment of structural condition it is also commonly measured in relation to a standard rolling wheel, constrained for convenience of measurement to move at creep speed. The advantage of techniques employing the rolling wheel is that they simulate the general pattern of stress–strain conditions generated by actual traffic.

An often-repeated criticism is that normal traffic does not move at the creep speed of the test procedures and that the dynamic response of bituminous road materials, whose stiffness is frequency dependent, is therefore not properly characterised. The strength of the criticism depends on the conditions in which pavement damage takes place. In the UK much of the damage is by deformation of the pavement layers and underlying subgrade: it takes place in warm and hot weather when the effective moduli of bituminous pavement layers are low. Broadly similar moduli are obtained when deflections are measured at creep speeds under the moderate pavement temperatures used for the sake of practical convenience.

The Deflection Beam

The best known test technique of the rolling wheel type is the Deflection Beam, originally designed by Benkelman[4] for use in the WASHO Road Test in the United States and since much modified in both design and in method of operation by different research organisations and road authorities. The basic layout of the beam is shown diagrammatically in Fig. 1. It is designed to pass between the dual rear wheels of a loaded lorry so that the vehicle can be driven slowly past, its tip resting on the road surface. The beam is pivoted at a third point along its length and the deflection of the road surface is detected by a dial gauge measuring the movement of the opposite end of the beam. The dial gauge and pivot are carried on a datum frame which rests on the road behind the load wheels. The maximum deflection as the wheels pass the measuring tip and the recovery reading after the wheels have moved away are noted. The deflection may be defined either as the mean of the two readings or as the recovery value only. An alternative method of operation is to place the measuring tip immediately between the dual wheels and to measure the recovery value as the wheels move away. This method is not recommended when the pavement contains an appreciable thickness of bituminous materials because the magnitude of the recovery deflection is affected by the length of time for which the wheels are stationary at the first point before the measurement is made.

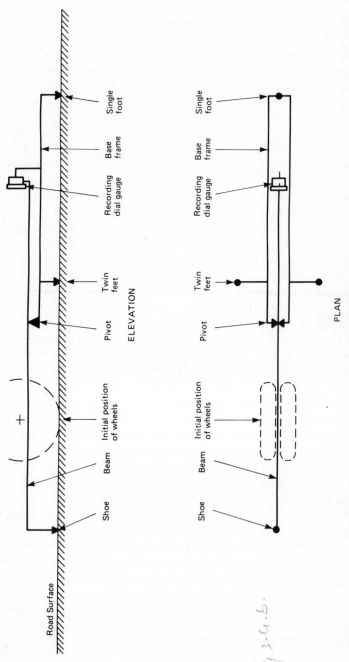

FIG. 1. Diagrammatic representation of the deflection beam. (Crown copyright, reproduced by permission of the Controller of HM Stationery Office.)

The shape of the deflected dish and hence the radius of curvature can be measured by replacing the dial gauge with some form of electrical displacement transducer and by providing a system for detecting and recording the movement of the load wheel in relation to the measurement of deflection. Although this is frequently done, the need for electrical recording detracts from the attractive simplicity of the original concept, and measurements inevitably take much longer to carry out.

Making two measurements at a point, an experienced team can take in excess of 250 measurements in a working day if they are reasonably closely spaced, say over a mile or two of road. This output was hailed as revolutionary when considered in relation to that obtainable with the conventional plate bearing test, the only measurement of pavement stiffness previously available. However, the test is still slow when considered in relation to the length of a road or road network, and mechanised automative versions of the Beam have since been successfully developed.

Automatic Methods of Deflection Measurement Under a Rolling Wheel
These are of two main types.

Travelling deflectometers: A form of Deflection Beam is mounted in front of each pair of dual rear wheels of a long articulated lorry. The Beams are carried on a large datum frame which stands stationary on the road, independent of the continuously moving lorry while the deflection generated by the approaching dual wheel is detected and recorded. The datum frames and beams are then carried rapidly forward relative to the lorry ready to begin the next cycle of measurement. Equipment of this type is in use in California[5] and Denmark.[6] The lorries operate at 1 to $1 \cdot 5 \, \text{km h}^{-1}$ taking measurements at 6 and 11 m intervals respectively. The complete influence line of deflection is recorded, in California on paper, and in Denmark on magnetic tape.

The Deflectograph: The Deflectograph, originally designed by the Laboratoire des Ponts et Chaussees in France, operates within the wheel base of a standard rigid wheel-base lorry and is thus shorter and more manoeuverable than are Deflectometers. Variants of this equipment are widely used: about 80 are in operation in at least 18 countries.

The principle of the pivoted beams supported by a datum frame is similar to that of the Deflection Beam but the dial gauge is replaced by an inductive displacement transducer recording the movement of a short beam

FIG. 2.   The Deflectograph.   (Crown copyright, reproduced by permission of the Controller of HM Stationery Office.)

incorporating a 7 to 1 reduction arm. The two beams, one in each wheel-path are mounted on a T-shaped datum frame resting on the road surface at its extremities. The whole assembly operates between the front and rear axles of a rigid lorry. During the measurement cycle it is stationary on the road, recording the deflection of the road surface as the dual rear wheels approach and pass the point of measurement. On the maximum deflection being achieved, it is pulled forward on steel skids at twice the speed of the lorry by a cable system, operated through an electro-mechanical clutch, to the next measuring point. A general view of a machine is shown in Fig. 2.

Systems for the analogue and digital recording of both maximum deflection and the shape of the deflected dish on the approach movement have been developed.

The measurements are spaced at 4 m intervals along the road and the vehicle moves at about 2 km h^{-1} giving a maximum daily route capacity of about 16 km.

Stationary Loading

The alternative approach to deflection measurement is by applying a load over a circular area at a fixed location in the road surface. Originally this took the form of a static test with the load applied slowly over a period using a hydraulic jack. This conventional plate loading test has now been superseded by speedier techniques which apply a dynamic load, either as a single pulse or repeatedly.

Tests of this kind generate stress–strain conditions which are not representative of conditions in the real road. The pavement is loaded by a pulse of constant duration irrespective of depth, and planes of principal stress do not rotate during loading, whereas under a rolling wheel load the duration of the load pulse increases with increasing depth and planes of principal stress rotate. The deflection response of materials which are frequency and stress dependent will therefore be effected. Inertial effects not present under a rolling wheel are also introduced. There is no general recognition of these differences and, where recognised, no agreement as to their importance. This will depend on the use made of the results; determination of layer moduli computed on the assumption of elastic behaviour will be incorrect to some extent.

Stationary Loading Techniques

Plate bearing tests: Conventional plate bearing equipment is sometimes used to load the pavement for the measurement of deflection. The pavement is usually subjected to a number of load cycles before the rebound deflection is measured. The procedure is very slow and therefore cannot be used to characterise a length of road in any detail.

The falling weight deflectometer:[7] This equipment, originally designed but not used in France and now employed in Holland and Denmark, drops a weight of 150 kg from a variable height on to a spring system; this, in turn, transmits a load pulse of about 28 ms (equivalent to about 34 Hz) to the road surface by means of a circular plate of 300 mm diameter. At the maximum drop height of 400 mm a peak load of 60 kN is developed. The deflection of the pavement is measured by velocity-sensitive displacement transducers, one at the centre of the loaded area and one or two others at fixed distances from the load.

The equipment is carried on a single axle trailer towed by a vehicle carrying the power supply and recording equipment. The vehicle also houses the controls for the loading cycle and for the operation of the hydraulic jacks used to raise the trailer when a test is being carried out. Maximum output is of the order of two hundred measurements per day.

The Dynaflect:[8] The Dynaflect consists of a small two-wheel trailer carrying a dynamic force generator in the form of two eccentric contra-rotating masses.

The dynamic force varies at a frequency of 8 Hz with a maximum value of 227 N: this is superimposed on a static load of 725 kg and is transmitted to the road surface through two small rigid wheels located 0·50 m apart. The maximum deflection midway between the wheels and at four other points along the centre-line between the wheels is measured by velocity sensitive transducers. Equipment for recording maximum deflection and the shape of the deflected dish are carried in a towing vehicle.

The equipment is capable of making 50 to 100 measurements daily. It is in use in several states of the United States and there are individual machines in several other countries.

The Road Rater:[9] In this equipment the varying load is generated by a hydraulic vibrator on the road reacting against an inertial mass of steel. A maximum dynamic force of 454 N operating at frequencies between 10 and 60 Hz is superimposed on a static load of 208 kg. The deflection under the load is measured by a velocity-sensitive transducer and other transducers can be used to determine the deflection profile. The equipment can be trailer mounted or carried on the front of a light vehicle which carries the hydraulic power supply and recording equipment. About 300 measurements at a single frequency or alternatively 100 at 3 frequencies are possible in a working day, the number being dependent on the spacing of the points of measurement.

The equipment is in use in several states of the United States and in Italy.

EMPLOYMENT OF SURVEY EQUIPMENT

The choice of a particular type of equipment for surveying the structural strength of a road will, of course, be influenced primarily by the design method with which it is to be used. It is important to realise that without an authoritative method and the ability of the test equipment to provide data input compatible with that method, other apparently advantageous features of specific items of equipment, such as convenience of operation or low first cost, are illusory.

It is, however, instructive to compare the available equipment in terms of their testing capacity as this is a most important factor in determining whether the measurement input to any design method is sufficient for the output of the method to be effective in designing strengthening measures.

The various stationary loading devices all have broadly comparable output of 100 to 300 readings per day, with the Dynaflect (the oldest equipment of this type) having the lowest productivity.

The repeated loading equipment has the disadvantage of applying unrealistically small loads in relation to those applied by lorry traffic but there should be no need for the repeat readings which can be necessary when single pulse equipment is used. Their output is only marginally better than that of the Deflection Beam when only deflection is measured, but if the shape of the deflection bowl is required, the output is substantially better than that of the Deflection Beam.

The daily output of the Deflectograph, about 4000 measurements per wheel-path, is far greater, and the simultaneous measurement it takes in each wheel-path presents a better overall picture of pavement condition than measurements in one wheel-path alone can give. The spacing between measurement is, however, fixed at 4 m, unlike those of all other types of equipment which can test at any selected spacing.

The length of road that can be surveyed with a stationary load device is greater than that with a Deflectograph only when measurements with the former are spaced at intervals of not less than 80 m (assuming 200 measurements per day and no repeat readings).

The basic requirement is that measurements should be spaced sufficiently close together to identify significant changes in structural condition along the road so that the strengthening recommendations can be matched as closely as possible to the differing strengthening requirements. The spacing should be much less than the minimum practical length of an overlay of a given thickness.

The required spacing will vary according to road condition: this is likely to be affected by changes in subgrade and pavement type and by drainage conditions. When the road condition is uniform, readings at more than a hundred meters will prove to be adequate and the use of a stationary loading technique, or perhaps the Deflection Beam could be preferable. At the other extreme the variation in condition and strength along the road will be sufficiently rapid that measurements should be spaced as closely as possible, i.e. every few metres. In the UK the variability of road strength is sufficiently rapid to make a close spacing desirable and the standard technique adopted with the Deflectograph is to characterise a road at 12 m intervals by meaning three successive measurements of deflection. This spacing allows accurate selection of overlay lengths to be made, and identification of short lengths of road sufficiently damaged to require partial reconstruction is also possible. For these conditions the Deflectograph can cover a much greater length of road per day than other techniques.

 ## DESIGN METHODS

A number of methods for the design of overlays have been published in the literature. These can broadly be divided into three categories:

(a) Methods based on engineering experience and judgement alone, i.e. without measurements of structural strength, where this experience and judgement has been formally codified. The most common approach is that of the equivalent thickness or 'index' method[10] in which the thickness and type of existing pavement layers are compared to the design of the new pavement required to carry the projected traffic, the overlay thickness being given by the difference. The process is often refined by inclusion of coefficients to modify the existing layer thicknesses according to a visual assessment of their structural condition.

(b) Empirical methods[11,12] based on measurements related to the structural strength of the road, most commonly to the deflection of the road surface, less frequently to its curvature. Overlay design thicknesses are those required to achieve a given level of deflection (and/or curvature)

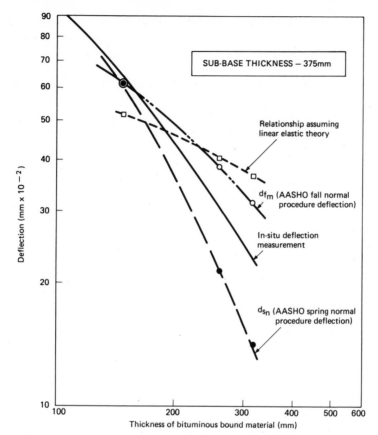

FIG. 3.   *In situ* and theoretical relationships between deflection and thickness of bituminous bound material. (Crown copyright, reproduced by permission of the Controller of HM Stationery Office.)

associated with satisfactory performance of the strengthened road under the expected traffic.

(c) Methods based on the same measured parameters but which adopt a structural or mechanistic approach for part of the design procedure.[13,14] Typically elastic theory will be used to calculate the overlay thickness required to reduce the deflection to a given level: limiting values of calculated stress or strain at critical levels in the pavement may also be correlated directly with road performance in terms of deformation and cracking. There is some uncertainty as to whether such an approach can be used directly however, as is illustrated by Fig. 3 where the reduction in deflection brought about by increasing the thickness of bituminous bound material using elastic theory is shown to be substantially smaller than that found by *in situ* measurement. The principal reason for the discrepancy is the difficulty of adequately modelling the subgrade condition. A number of proposals have been made to overcome the problem but these methods are empirical and in general have not been validated nor can they be theoretically substantiated. The use of a purely theoretical approach is therefore open to some doubt and should only be used if empirical data is not available. A possible exception is pavements containing a cement bound layer of high modulus which substantially reduces the effect of the subgrade condition in the analysis. More complete mechanistic treatment requires the use of models capable of predicting the development of deformation and fatigue cracking in both new and strengthened pavements.

Methods based on engineering judgement have generally been adequate while traffic levels remained light by today's standards and where the pavements to be strengthened were of one basic type, i.e. having the traditional crushed stone base beneath a thin bituminous surfacing. There are no significant recent developments of this type of method, and descriptions will therefore be confined to two of wider application and recent development, one each in categories (b) and (c).

TRRL DEFLECTION METHOD

With the aim of gaining widespread acceptance by the large number of Road Authorities responsible for pavement strengthening in the UK the emphasis was placed on developing a method based primarily on a straightforward technique of *in situ* measurement of structural strength and, where necessary, supported by simple laboratory and field measurements of materials properties and condition. At that time little was known about the stress–strain behaviour of road pavements; any fundamental approach was out of the question and direct correlation between deflection and road performance was investigated using the recently developed Deflection Beam associated with a wheel load of 3·175 kg. Deflection was considered to be likely to correlate, at least in a broad sense, with the performance of pavements in the UK which, on roads carrying medium and heavy traffic, deteriorate primarily by deformation; a rolling wheel was preferred to a stationary technique of measurement because of its greater realism.

A programme of testing designed to standardise the test technique and to investigate systematically the relation between deflection and road performance was initiated on the full scale road experiments built by the Transport and Road Research Laboratory; these contain a wide range of combinations of pavement materials and thicknesses. Over 340 experimental sections have been regularly tested in addition to about 30 short lengths of main road whose construction is of particular interest. Their behaviour has been studied[15] in terms of their deflection history, i.e. the evaluation of their deflection as measured and defined in a standard manner and their deterioration under known traffic expressed in terms of deformation in the wheel-paths and any cracking which developed there.

Deflection Measurement

Measurements made in the early months after opening for traffic often changed considerably with time as granular materials compacted and the subgrade moisture regions recovered from the disturbance of construction. Thereafter, measurements in spring, when temperatures suitable for deflection measurements coincide with high water-tables and therefore weak subgrade conditions, show acceptable consistency. Measurements in autumn are also little different except when preceded by abnormally hot and prolonged summers.

The Effect of Temperature

Chapters 1–3 in the first book in the series demonstrated the importance of temperature in influencing the stiffness of bituminous materials and hence the deflection of flexible pavements. It is therefore important, both for the purposes of comparison and design, to reduce deflection measurements made at different temperatures on the road to equivalent deflections at a standard temperature. The susceptibility of pavement deflection to temperature change will vary according to the proportion of pavement stiffness which is contributed by the layers of bituminous material. As a result different temperature correction curves are required for different pavements.

It did not prove practical to establish the susceptibilities of all the pavements in the full scale road experiments from pilot-scale pavements in the laboratory under controlled conditions of temperature. However, as the road experiments matured it was noted that the plot of deflection versus temperature, measured 40 mm below the pavement surface, provided a valuable indicator of the operative temperature susceptibility. Figure 4 gives typical results from a pavement whose structural stiffness at constant temperature changed only slowly with time and traffic. The scatter

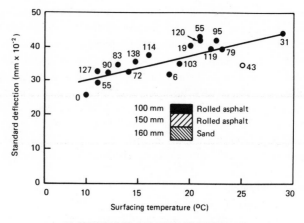

(a) EXAMPLE OF A SECTION OF VIRTUALLY
CONSTANT STRUCTURAL STIFFNESS

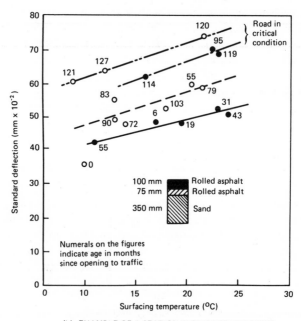

(b) EXAMPLE OF A SECTION WITH DETERIORATING
STRUCTURAL STIFFNESS

FIG. 4. Temperature susceptibility. (Crown copyright, reproduced by permission
of the Controller of HM Stationery Office.)

represents both real differences in deflection and experimental error superimposed on a very slowly rising trend of deflection with time. Figure 4 also shows the pattern of data obtained on an initially weaker pavement whose stiffness decreases relatively rapidly as the pavement deteriorates to a structurally critical condition. In both cases, linear relations between deflection and temperature are obtained for the temperature range between 10 and 30 °C; the slope of the relation (temperature susceptibility) increases with increasing deflection level. These relationships form the basis of temperature correction charts which enable deflections of a given pavement type measured at any temperature between 10 and 30 °C to be adjusted to a standard reference temperature of 20 °C.[16] The charts are of acceptable accuracy except when used on pavements founded on very strong or very weak soils tested at temperatures at the extremes of the normal working range. In these cases check measurements of deflection at another temperature are recommended.

Assessment of Pavement Performance

The spectra of axle loads which passed over the roads were translated into damage spectra using the load-equivalence factors given in Road Note 29[17] and the total damage potential of the traffic expressed in terms of 'standard' axle loads of 8200 kg. On the majority of road experiments data from dynamic weighbridges[18] enables the load spectra to be measured directly; on the few experiments without this facility and on non-experimental roads traffic census data and estimates of the composition of commercial traffic were used.

The deterioration of the pavements was defined primarily in terms of the development of deformation in the wheel-paths. Cracking, where it occurred, took place relatively late in the life of the pavement. A systematic study was made of the relation between deflection and the development of deterioration up to the stage where the pavement was considered to be failed, at a rut depth of about 20 mm. This showed that the rut depths developed steadily to values in excess of 10 mm, thereafter further deterioration to failure was less predictable. Deflection increased slowly but subsequently increased more rapidly as structural deterioration accelerated to failure. By comparison of deflection and deformation behaviour a critical stage in the life of a pavement could be defined when damage to the pavement was limited and when its life could be extended economically by an overlay of moderate thickness. This critical condition corresponded to a rut of about 10–12 mm after the road had carried about 75 % of the traffic needed to bring about pavement failure. This criterion was adopted in

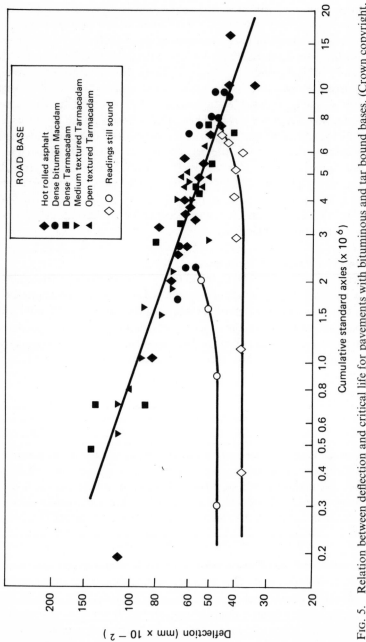

FIG. 5.   Relation between deflection and critical life for pavements with bituminous and tar bound bases. (Crown copyright, reproduced by permission of the Controller of HM Stationery Office.)

developing deflection histories; it was modified when the subsequent pavement behaviour demonstrated that the observed rutting or cracking was superficial rather than structural, in origin.

A typical deflection history reflects changes in the subgrade following the disturbance of the construction phase and compaction of granular layers. Normally an equilibrium deflection is attained within a year of opening to traffic, or earlier if the subgrade is sealed very early during construction. Thus deflection, measurable in spring and autumn, behaves systematically with increasing time and traffic and has been used for the prediction of the lives of both new and overlaid pavements.

Relations Between Deflection and Performance

Typical deflection histories are shown on Fig. 5 for two pavements with bituminous roadbases; the initial measurements have been omitted. The measurements increase slowly to the onset of critical conditions. Each filled point on the diagram indicates the deflection at the critical life of a pavement. The results were obtained from six road experiments and cover a wide range of rolled asphalt, bitumen-macadam, and tarmacadam roadbases. The complete deflection history for each pavement has been omitted for the sake of clarity. Also omitted are the results obtained on a large number of other pavements which are still in a structural sound condition and whose deflection histories remain beneath the strongly defined relationship between deflection and critical life.

The results were obtained on subgrades of strength of between 2 and 15 % CBR (California Bearing Ratio), with most lying between 3 and 8 %.

Other factors such as the thickness and type of sub-base, the thickness of roadbase, and type of surfacing had no significant effect on the common relation. The deflection–life relation in Fig. 5 and the trend lines of the deflection histories to the common critical line have been used to prepare the chart on Fig. 6 which is capable of predicting at any time in the life of a pavement type the onset of critical conditions from a knowledge of deflection, cumulative traffic which has used the road to date, and basic type of pavement construction. The dotted zones for the lowest and very highest traffic volumes are obtained by extrapolation of the experimental relation between deflection w and life L of the form

$$w = \frac{A}{L^N}$$

where A and N are constants.

These deflection–life relations are unlikely to be valid for thin pavements

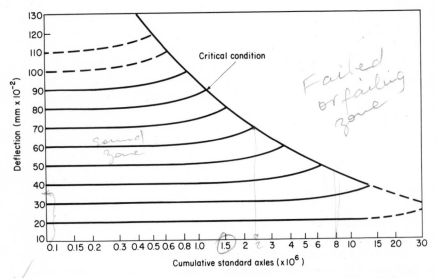

FIG. 6.   Design chart for pavements with bituminous and tar bound bases. (Crown copyright, reproduced by permission of the Controller of HM Stationery Office.)

with deflections of greater than about 120×10^{-2} mm as fatigue cracking would then be the controlling criterion. Similar systematic studies on pavements with granular roadbases and rolled asphalt and macadam surfacings between 70 and 110 mm thick revealed a very similar pattern of deflection–performance relationship. The range of sub-grade strengths involved was similar to that for bituminous bases. The only exception to the general pattern was the behaviour of granular roadbases using granite aggregates which lack cementing action. They are more flexible and can sustain greater deflections before reaching a critical condition. The design chart developed was little different from that for pavements with bituminous roadbases; this is gratifying in view of the fact that both types of road belong to one broad class of pavement differing only in the proportion of the bituminous and granular materials they contain.

Deterioration of pavements containing lean concrete roadbases begin by cracking in the roadbase itself, as discussed by Williams,[27] but the first sign of damage on the road surface is conventional rutting because the substantial thicknesses of bituminous surfacing materials inhibit the propagation of cracks to the road surface; some proportion of the rut is, of course, contributed by the surfacing itself. Development of cracking in the cemented roadbase is normally a gradual process and results in a steady increase in measured deflections until critical conditions are reached. The design chart developed for use with lean concrete roadbases[19] is similar in form to those for the other types of roadbase but associates considerably lower deflection values with a given life; this is to be expected in view of the very different nature of the cemented roadbase.

Overlay Design

To specify the thickness of overlay required to extend the life of a road for a given time and traffic from a knowledge of its deflection, it is necessary to establish both the reduction in deflection brought about by overlays of various thicknesses and also the deflection/performance relationships of the overlaid pavements; there is no reason to assume that these relationships should be the same as for new pavements. The general approach has been described in ref. 16. Information from overlays applied to the laboratory's full scale road experiments[20] when these are retired from normal observation has been supplemented by observation of overlays laid as normal maintenance practice. Information on deflection reduction has also been obtained from studies on pilot-scale pavements and from relations between thickness and deflection derived from road experiments.

Reduction in Deflection by Overlays
The reduction in deflection brought about by overlaying is normally derived from overall trends of deflection established over several years before and after overlaying. Measurements restricted to immediate before-and-after studies, particularly if the overlay is applied in the summer, can give misleading results. Figure 7 demonstrates that the true deflection reduction can only be established with certainty from a series of measurements.

The results obtained indicate that deflection is largely independent of sub-grade stiffness in the range CBR 2·5 to 15% and also of the type and thickness of the overlay material. The design chart evolved is shown in Fig. 8. Also plotted on the chart are typical results obtained from an overlay on a road experiment and from deflection/thickness relations given in ref. 16.

Provisional recommendations for the deflection reduction brought about by dense bitumen-macadam are shown on the same diagram by dotted lines; the information has been derived by pilot-scale studies and from the overlaying of a short length of full scale road experiment.

Deflection—Performance Relations for Overlaid Pavements
Data for overlaid pavements with granular bases has enabled the relation

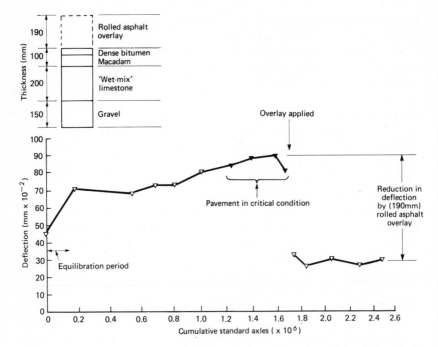

FIG. 7. A deflection history indicating the effect of a substantial rolled asphalt overlay. (Crown copyright, reproduced by permission of the Controller of HM Stationery Office.)

between early-life deflection and critical life to be determined. It is very similar to the relation for new granular construction. The same similarity applies for the critical deflection curve and enables the prediction chart of Fig. 9 to be used for overlaid pavements with reasonable confidence.

Of the numerous overlaid pavements having bituminous and lean concrete roadbases, none have so far reached a critical condition, although a number have reached positions in terms of deflection and cumulative traffic which are close to the relations between critical deflection and life obtained on new construction for these pavement types. In developing overlay designs for pavements with bituminous and lean concrete roadbases the deflection/life relations on both new and overlaid pavements are taken to be similar as has been shown to be the case for granular roadbases. It is considered that this assumption may be somewhat conservative in practice and will be modified accordingly if justified by future observed performance of overlays.

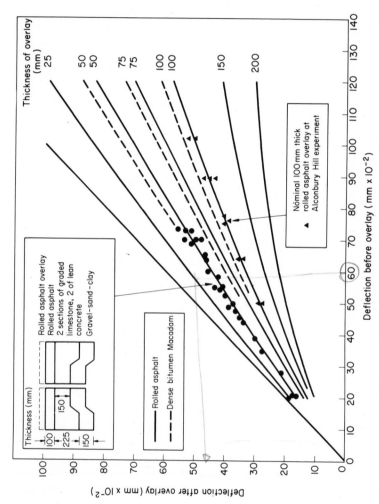

FIG. 8.   The reduction in deflection derived from structural relationships obtained on full scale road experiments and from overlay studies. (Crown copyright, reproduced by permission of the Controller of HM Stationery Office.)

Design Charts

The information, briefly reviewed above has been assimilated into two overlay design charts, one is for pavements with granular and bituminous roadbases, Fig. 9, and the second for lean concrete roadbases.[19] The thickness of rolled asphalt overlay can be determined from a knowledge of the traffic to be carried, expressed in standard axles, and the deflection of

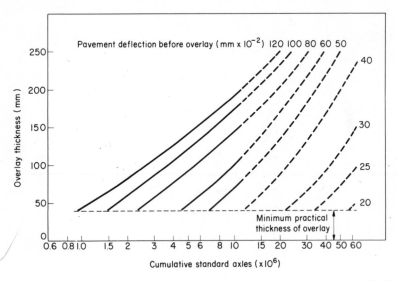

FIG. 9. Thickness of overlay required to achieve a given extension of life for existing pavements with granular and bituminous bases. (Crown copyright, reproduced by permission of the Controller of HM Stationery Office.)

the road. Other slightly different design charts are also available for strengthening roads having non-cementing granular bases and for strengthening with the dense macadam overlays used on some less heavily trafficked roads (for new construction this material is restricted to roads designed to carry less than $2 \cdot 5 \times 10^6$ standard axles).

In developing the overlay design chart for pavements with lean concrete bases it has been assumed that, where a substantial thickness of overlay is recommended, the strengthened pavement will perform, in terms of the deflection life relation, as if it were a pavement with granular or bituminous base. For overlay thicknesses in excess of 175 mm the relationships between overlay thickness and future life have therefore been adjusted towards the relationships for bituminous and granular bases.

The Method

The core of the design procedure is embodied in Figs. 6 and 9. The input to the method is deflection corrected to 20 °C measured at intervals along a road which are sufficiently closely spaced to ensure characterisation of the pavement strength and the way in which it varies along the length of the road. The deflection may be measured by the Deflection Beam or the Deflectograph, although in the latter case the deflection measured must be corrected to equivalent Deflection Beam deflections.

The number of commercial vehicles which have used the road since construction or last major strengthening together with the corrected deflection is used as input to Fig. 6 from which the unexpired life of the existing pavement may be estimated. If this life is insufficient to carry the anticipated future traffic then Fig. 9 is used to assess the overlay thickness required.

The Selection of the Most Economic Combination of Strengthening Measures

To ensure maximum economy, recommendations for strengthening measures must take into account the practical constraints imposed by the road situation.

The overlay design charts enable strengthening recommendations to be made for a pavement of a given level of deflection. However, deflection surveys on most roads in need of strengthening are characterised by large variations in deflection levels along the road as well as by high deflections. These variations can occur very rapidly. In contrast, the ideal strengthened road should be one whose deflection level is as constant as possible along its length so that future strengthening can be carried out with maximum economy using a relatively thin overlay on a pavement of uniform strength. It is therefore not practically possible to match the variation in deflection along a road by strengthening measures which are exactly appropriate at all points, but the output from the Deflectograph is sufficiently closely spaced for the results to be suitable for use in a practical engineering design procedure capable of eliminating the risk of localised early failure in the strengthened pavement and of over design of overlay thickness.

The method is at present based on the assumption that the use of the design chart appropriate to the pavement considered, guarantees that the specified overlay life will be achieved. Thus if it is required to ensure that not more than 10 % of the length of the road deteriorates to a critical condition before a specified life is achieved, it is only necessary to calculate the deflection level which defines the upper 10 % of deflections in the surveyed length. However, the distribution of deflections along a length of road is rarely found to be random; normally there is a greater probability of a high deflection being followed by a second high value than by a low value, and the converse is also true, i.e. they are statistically persistent. It is therefore necessary to guard against the possibility that, the top 10 % of deflections do not occur in a continuous length of road. This is ensured by dividing the survey length into the relatively short sections of 100 m for analysis.

It is also equally important that the top 10 % of deflections are not sufficiently high to bring about relatively early failure of parts of the overlay. This problem is overcome by defining the earliest point in time during the planned overlay life at which this can occur and then using this reduced life in conjunction with the overlay thickness already defined to determine from the design charts the present deflection that will ensure that this overlay will guarantee at least the reduced life. The present deflection thus calculated should exceed all measured deflections. Where this is not so, critical conditions will occur before the end of the reduced life, and some form of partial reconstruction is then required on these short lengths of high deflection.

The input to the proposed system is the overlay design life, the maximum percentage of the unit lengths of road into which the road is divided for analysis that can approach a critical condition before this life is achieved, the earliest time at which the percentage can approach a critical condition, and the costs of overlaying and reconstruction. Areas of high deflection are located for local reconstruction and overlays designed on the basis of 12 mm steps in thickness. The minimum discounted cost solution for each unit length is calculated and summed before the process is repeated with the analysis commencing at different start points. The proposals for the minimum total cost solution are then produced, together with a tabulation including the cost of all options investigated.

The output can then be passed to the maintenance engineers for them to identify and eliminate those strengthening options that are unacceptable for practical reasons, e.g. changes in overlay thickness may lead to problems of rainfall run-off. At this stage the maintenance history at the disposal of the engineer can identify overlay designs which are invalid for other reasons; in particular, high deflections associated with poor subgrade drainage should not be reduced by overlaying unless improvement in the drainage system proves to be impossible.

Finally, costs associated with strengthening that can only be assigned from local knowledge, such as those associated with raising kerbs, can be added so that the cheapest solutions suited to the requirements of the particular job can be established. These strengthening measures should form part of the overall maintenance strategy discussed in Chapter 5.

Validation of the Method

So far, the method has been used primarily to design strengthening measures on the basis of a single deflection survey on roads whose cumulative standard axles are estimated. Errors in estimation of past traffic of more than 30% are possible and this should be borne in mind when considering the following comparisons between the design curves and the results of deflection surveys.

Figure 10 gives results from a Deflectograph survey on two lengths of heavily trafficked road constructed with a lean-concrete base. The two lengths were opened at different times and were sited on subgrades of very different strength. Trial excavations were carried out in association with the deflection survey and the condition of the base was also investigated using wave-propagation techniques.[21] A summary of this information and of the visual survey of the surface is given for five lengths in Fig. 10. It will be seen that the condition of the lengths is closely represented by their proximity to the critical condition line.

More detailed information on a 2·5 km length of a strengthening project is given in Fig. 11. The initial survey was an early one (1966) and was carried out with the Benkelman Deflection Beam at 17 m intervals along the road rather than at the 12 m spacings recommended whenever practically possible and, of course, always achieved with the 'mean-of-three' results system normally adopted with the Deflectograph. This early example has been selected for illustration because the cumulative traffic on the strengthened road has now exceeded that which present design would indicate as being the life of the pavement before it should require a further strengthening.

The 2·5 km length is taken from a major road 35 km long, built to standards which are now considered to be inadequate both as to thickness and type of pavement materials used. The construction on the length considered was 40 mm rolled asphalt wearing course, 100 mm bitumen-macadam basecourse, 75 mm single-sized crushed limestone base, and 250–380 mm sand sub-base. Subgrade types are given in the figure.

Damage by rutting and cracking visible at the surface was extensive, and in an attempt to restore ride and strengthen the road the 40 mm wearing course had been replaced with a new rolled asphalt wearing course of low stone content just before the deflection survey was carried out. The survey showed the wide variation in deflection values, the majority lying in the

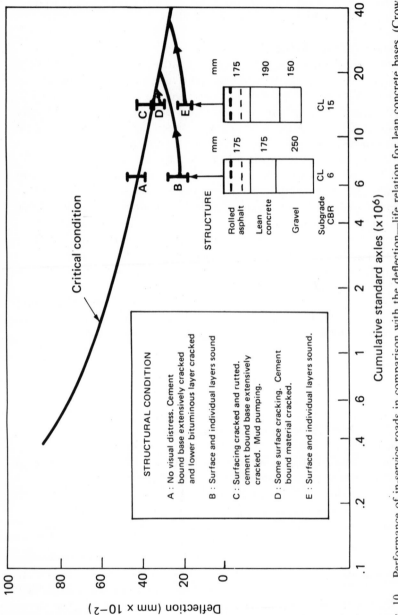

FIG. 10. Performance of in-service roads in comparison with the deflection—life relation for lean concrete bases. (Crown copyright, reproduced by permission of the Controller of HM Stationery Office.)

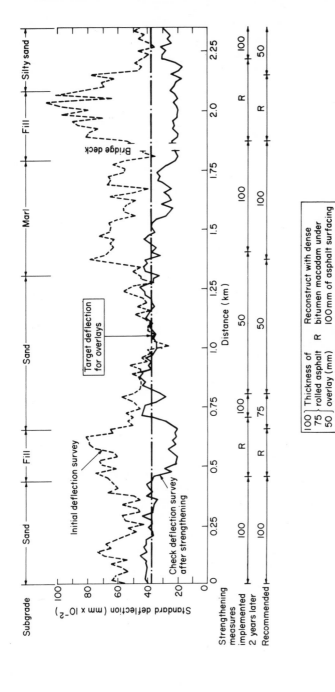

Fig. 11. Deflection surveys before and after strengthening operations based on the deflection approach. (Crown copyright, reproduced by permission of the Controller of HM Stationery Office.)

range 40–70 $\times$ 10^{-2} mm with two lengths giving appreciably higher values. Deflection levels were generally related to subgrade type and conditions as indicated by construction records. A ten-year overlay life under the estimated traffic was 6 $\times$ 10^6 standard axles using the recommendations then in current use. The target deflection of 38 $\times$ 10^{-2} mm could be achieved by overlay thicknesses in the range 50 to 100 mm over much of the road. The weakest lengths required overlays of greater than 100 mm thickness; these were precluded because of limited bridge clearance and reconstruction with a dense bitumen-macadam base under 100 mm of rolled asphalt was the best practical alternative.

The recommendations made and also the measures actually implemented two years later are shown in Fig. 11; the latter closely followed the recommendations, except beyond the 2·25 km position, where a 100 mm overlay was used to maintain a constant surface profile between two reconstructed lengths.

A further deflection survey designed to check the deflection reduction achieved was made by Deflectograph after the strengthening had been carried out in 1968; this is shown by the solid deflection profile on Fig. 11. It will be seen that a consistent deflection level was achieved over most of the overlaid length where the overlay thickness followed the recommendations. The level of deflection was however slightly greater than the target value more often than expected. This is because of the longer than average delay of two years in implementing the results of the survey, during which time further appreciable deterioration of the pavement took place, presumably accompanied by some increase in deflection levels. The use of a 100 mm overlay beyond the 2·25 km position instead of the recommended value of 50 mm reduced deflections well below the target value in a consistent manner.

The form of reconstruction selected by the Road Authority was a 250 mm dense bitumen-macadam base under a 100 mm rolled asphalt surfacing. As would be expected the reconstructed pavement was much stiffer than the overlaid lengths and the mean deflection of 20 $\times$ 10^{-2} mm obtained on the reconstructed length would be expected to give an overlay life of greater than 13 $\times$ 10^{-6} standard axles. Partial reconstruction of surfacing and base to give a life equal to that of the adjacent overlaid lengths would be more economic.

The expected growth of traffic on the strengthened road was greater than forecast and the design life of the overlaid lengths, according to *present* recommendations, of 6·3 $\times$ 10^6 standard axles had been exceeded by the end of 1975. The road was deemed to be in need of further strengthening in

1975 because of deterioration of the overlaid lengths after 5.8×10^6 standard axles. The agreement between prediction and practice was therefore acceptably good.

Status of the Method

1976 saw the publication of a Technical Memorandum by the Department of Transport[22] which recommended that deflection surveys be used both to design strengthening measures where necessary on Trunk Roads and Motorways and also to obtain an assessment of the structural condition of all those roads in order to assist in the formal planning of their maintenance and strengthening.

THE SHELL METHOD

The Shell method for determining structural maintenance requirements[23] is primarily based on their design procedure for new pavements.[24] It assumes that the pavement structure can be represented in general by a three layer linear elastic system in which the materials are homogeneous and isotropic.

The response of the existing pavement is defined by the maximum deflection and a deflection measured at a fixed distance from the maximum (an offset deflection) produced under standard loading conditions. This information is obtained by the Falling Weight Deflectometer.

Charts have been prepared that give the relationship between the modulus and thickness of the asphalt layer together with the measured maximum and offset deflections for pre-determined values of the moduli of the unbound or cement-bound layers of the pavement and the modulus of the subgrade. A fixed relationship between the modulus of the unbound layers and that of the subgrade is assumed. Given the two measured parameters, together with a measure of the thickness of the unbound layer and an estimate of the modulus of the asphalt, it is possible to determine the subgrade modulus and hence the modulus of the unbound layer and the effective asphalt thickness. A procedure is also presented[23] for pavements incorporating cement-bound layers and asphalt-bound layers of differing properties when the fixed relationship between subgrade modulus and the modulus of the upper pavement layer cannot be assumed.

The influence of temperature on the measured deflection parameters is taken into account by identifying sections of road with a uniform temperature, and correcting for temperature by modifying the estimated modulus of the asphalt (rather than correcting the measured deflection).

The derived subgrade modulus and effective asphalt thickness, together with the assumed asphalt modulus and measured roadbase thickness are then used as input to The Shell Pavement Design Method to determine the design life of the pavement. This life is compared with the traffic carried at the time of the survey; an estimate of residual life can then be made. If the residual life is less than the required future life the Design Method Charts are used to determine the total thickness of asphalt, overlay thickness plus effective asphalt thickness necessary to achieve a design life equal to the past traffic plus the future traffic.

This procedure assumes that the stiffness of the unbound layers and subgrade at the time of test have not deteriorated from their original condition; also that a thickness of asphalt, equal to the difference in effective and actual thicknesses has a strength equal only to that of unbound base. These two assumptions are both conservative; the first producing an under-estimate of residual life and the latter an over-estimate of the overlay thickness necessary.

Validation of the Method

Published validation of the design procedure[23,24] is largely limited to a comparison of predicted and observed existing layer thicknesses and moduli. These results give excellent agreement. There is at present no published data that directly substantiates the aspects of the method relevant to prediction of overlay life. Indirect information on these is, however, available[25] by comparing the overlay thicknesses required by the Shell method and the TRRL method at a number of sites in the UK which have been surveyed by both the Falling Weight Deflectometer and the Deflectograph. The overlay thickness derived by the Shell method are about 50% larger than those obtained for the TRRL method and there is some discrepancy between the two methods in the ranking they give to the various sites in regard to the overlay thickness required.

The Shell method has been derived for use on a world-wide basis and in particular for use in areas where there is little or no information on local criteria. It is not surprising therefore that the method is less precise than a method specifically related to the materials, construction techniques and environment associated with roads in the UK. In addition the Shell method has shown itself to be conservative in comparison to the TRRL method and this is likely to be the case in general. Its use is therefore unlikely to produce costly mistakes and it must be regarded as a significant maintenance tool for use in countries without a developed and validated local method.

FINAL COMMENTS

There are a number of methods available for measuring the structural condition of existing pavements in terms of the deflection and curvature of the road surface. They measure quantities related, but not equal to, the dynamic response of a road under moving traffic. The suitability of a particular method of measurement for design purposes depends on the availability of an appropriate design method and on the ability of the equipment to determine rapidly the varying pavement stiffnesses of long lengths of road.

In the UK an empirical method relating deflection to road performance and to the required overlay design thickness is now operational: there is considerable practical evidence of its validity.

Further developments in design methods will probably involve increasing use of curvature as an additional parameter of pavement performance, the use of structural design procedures in introducing new and improved overlay materials and for designing the partial reconstruction of badly damaged major roads, and the introduction of probabilistic concepts in design.

REFERENCES

1. OUTER, P., REICHERT, J and VERSTRAETEN, J. Les critères de qualité des chaussées et leur dimensionnement, 11th Congress ARCBR, Ghent, 1965.
2. LISTER, N. W. and JONES, R. The behaviour of flexible pavements under moving wheel loads, Proc. 2nd Int. Conf. on the Struct. Design of Asphalt Pavements, **1**, 1021–35, Univ. of Michigan, Ann Arbor, 1967.
3. LEGER, P. and AUTRET, P. The use of deflection measurements for the structural design and supervision of pavements, Proc. 3rd Int. Conf. on the Struct. Design of Asphalt Pavements, **1**, 1188–204, Univ. of Michigan, Ann Arbor, 1972.
4. The WASHO Road Test, Hwy Res. Brd, Special Reports 18 and 22, 1955.
5. ZUBE, E. and FORSYTH, R. Flexible pavement maintenance requirements as determined by deflection measurements, Hwy Res. Brd, Record No. 129, 1966.
6. BARENHOLT, E. Bearing capacity investigation by Deflectograph, 15th Permanent Int. Ass. of Road Congresses, World Road Congress, Mexico City, 1975.

7. BOHN, A., ULLIDTZ, P., STUBSTAD, R. and SORENSEN, A. Danish experiments with the French Falling Weight Deflectometer, Proc. 3rd Int. Conf. on the Struct. Design of Asphalt Pavements, 1, 1119–28, Univ. of Michigan, Ann Arbor, 1972.

8. SCRIVNER, F. H., SWIFT, G. and MOORE, W. H. A new research tool for measuring pavement deflections, Hwy Res. Brd, Record No. 129, 1966.

9. BHAJANDAS, A. C., CUMBERLEDGE, G. and HOFFMAN, G. L. Flexible pavement evaluation and rehabilitation, Amer. Soc. Civ. Engrs, *J. of Transp. Eng.*, **103**, TE1, Proc. paper 12689, 75–85, Jan. 1977.

10. THE ASPHALT INSTITUTE. Asphalt overlays and pavement rehabilitation, Asphalt Institute Manual No. 17 (MS-17), College Park, Maryland, 1969.

11. TEST METHOD 356-D. Methods of test to determine overlay requirements by pavement deflection measurements, California Division of Highways, Sacramento, California, 1973.

12. BHAJANDAS, A. C., CUMBERLEDGE, G., HOFFMAN, G. L. and HOPKINS, J. G. A practical approach to flexible pavement evaluation and rehabilitation, Proc. 4th Int. Conf. on the Struct. Design of Asphalt Pavements, 1, 665–72, Univ. of Michigan, Ann Arbor, 1977.

13. TREYBIG, H. J., McCULLOUGH, B. F., FINN, F. N. and McCOMB, R. Design of asphalt concrete overlays using layer theory, Proc. 4th Int. Conf. on the Struct. Design of Asphalt Pavements, 1, 589–627, Univ. of Michigan, Ann Arbor, 1977.

14. RUFFORD, P. G. A pavement analysis and structural design procedure based on deflection, Proc. 4th Int. Conf. on the Struct. Design of Asphalt Pavements, 1, 710–20, Univ. of Michigan, Ann Arbor, 1977.

15. LISTER, N. W. Deflection criteria for flexible pavements, TRRL Report No. LR 375, Dept. of the Environment, Transport and Road Research Laboratory, Crowthorne, 1972.

16. LISTER, N. W. Deflection criteria for flexible pavements and the design of overlays, Proc. 3rd Int. Conf. on the Struct. Design of Asphalt Pavements, 1, 1206–26, Univ. of Michigan, Ann Arbor, 1972.

17. ROAD RESEARCH LABORATORY. A guide to the structural design of pavements for new roads, Road Note No. 29, 3rd ed., Dept. of the Environment, HMSO, London, 1970.

18. TROTT, J. J. and GRAINGER, J. W. Design of a dynamic weighbridge for recording vehicle wheel loads, TRRL Report No. LR 219, Dept. of the Environment, Transport and Road Research Laboratory, Crowthorne, 1968.

19. LISTER, N. W. and KENNEDY, C. K. A system for the prediction of pavement life and design of pavement strengthening, Proc. 4th Int. Conf. on the Struct. Design of Asphalt Pavements, 1, 629–48, Univ. of Michigan, Ann Arbor, 1977.

20. SALT, G. F. Recent full-scale flexible pavement design experiments in Britain, Proc. 2nd Int. Conf. on the Struct. Design of Asphalt Pavements, 1, 1069–85, Iniv. of Michigan, Ann Arbor, 1967.

21. JONES, R., THROWER, E. N. and GATFIELD, E. N. The surface wave method, Proc. 2nd Int. Conf. on the Struct. Design of Asphalt Pavements, 505–19, Univ. of Michigan, Ann Arbor, 1967.

22. DEPARTMENT OF TRANSPORT. Deflection measurements and their application to

structural maintenance and overlay design for flexible pavements, Technical Memórandum H10/76, Dept. of Transport, London, 1976.

23. CLAESSEN, A. I. M. and DITMARSCH, R. Pavement evaluation and overlay design, Proc. 4th Int. Conf. on the Struct. Design of Asphalt Pavements, **1,** 649–61, Univ. of Michigan, Ann Arbor, 1977.

24. CLAESSEN, A. I. M., EDWARDS, J. M., SOMMER, P. and UGE, R. Asphalt pavement design—The Shell Method, Proc. 4th Int. Conf. on the Struct. Design of Asphalt Pavements, **1,** 39–73, Univ. of Michigan, Ann Arbor, 1977.

25. CLAESSEN, A. I. M., VALKERING, C. P. and DITMARSCH, R. Pavement evaluation with the Falling Weight Deflectometer, Proc. Ass. Asphalt Paving Technol., **45,** 122–54, 1976.

26. PEATTIE, K. R. Flexible pavement design, Chapter 1, in *Developments in Highway Pavement Engineering*—1, P. S. Pell (ed.), Applied Science Publishers, London, 1978.

27. WILLIAMS, R. I. T. Cement stabilised materials, Chapter 5, in *Developments in Highway Pavement Engineering*—1, P. S. Pell (ed.), Applied Science Publishers, London, 1978.

Chapter 5

PAVEMENT MAINTENANCE MANAGEMENT

BRIAN COX

Lincolnshire County Council, UK

SUMMARY

The purpose of this chapter is to consider a systematic approach for the management of pavement maintenance incorporating all the processes involved in the formulation of pavement maintenance programmes and the application of those processes in a manner which recognises their inter-relationship and optimises their potential contribution to economically effective decision making.

The system discussed uses available techniques and processes, and its implementation provides an efficient and effective use of the available funds arising from objective and consistent selection of road sections for treatment, improved use of materials, and the optimisation of the choice of treatment in terms of cost, resources, social impact, etc. The result is that the engineer can manage a highway network with some assurance that priorities for treatment are in the right order and that the right materials are put down in the right place at the right time.

INTRODUCTION

Under traffic the deterioration of a pavement becomes apparent in various ways. With time the pavement becomes unable to resist deformation and cracking, its load bearing capacity decreases and if this tendency is not remedied the eventual consequence will normally be complete structural failure necessitating total reconstruction. During the process of deterioration the road surface exhibits visible signs of distress such as cracking, rutting in the wheel tracks, or a generally uneven surface. Pot-holing may also occur. The road user experiences a decreasing level of service in terms of riding comfort and the spray hazard from water in ruts which can also lead to skidding accidents. Pedestrians on footways adjoining rutted carriageways suffer from spray and the occupants of adjacent properties experience increased noise from traffic on uneven surfaces.

It should be mentioned that rutting and an uneven surface can be produced by weakness of the pavement surfacing or differential sub-grade movement so that such signs are not necessarily indicative of structural failure. However, in all cases remedial treatment is required as a pavement deteriorates in order to extend its life and to remedy the disbenefits experienced by those using and those affected by the road.

The Standing Committee on Highway Maintenance established by the Department of Transport, the Association of Metropolitan Authorities, and the Association of County Councils has stated:

> Maintenance should be defined as operations intended to delay the deterioration of or restore a road to a condition appropriate to provide its past level of service.

Various processes are commonly used to delay deterioration:

(a)   Repairs of local surfacing failure, evidenced by the loss of material which form pot-holes, is commonly carried out on a routine basis with similar material.

(b)   Full construction depth repairs to remedy localised structural failure of the pavement are carried out on a programmed basis. The success of all forms of patching is dependent on close attention to method and materials since ideally the homogeneous nature of the pavement structure should be preserved. Preferred methods have been established and fully described.[1]

(c)   Surface dressing is used to seal crazed surfaces against the weakening effect upon the pavement structure of the ingress of water and to restore skidding resistance. Successful application involves consideration of the binder, chippings, and the application techniques. The range of sideway force coefficient (SFC) values obtained in practice with a variety of chippings is shown in Fig. 1. Guidance on surface dressing can be obtained from the Transport and Road Research Laboratory (TRRL) Road Note[2] and the

Surface Dressing
typical class 2 road

B. F. SLAG _____ 0 · 64

STEEL SLAG _____ 0 · 44

QUARTZITE GRAVEL (crushed) _____ 0 · 67

FLINT GRAVEL _____ 0 · 61

GRANITE 'A' _____ 0 · 67

GRANITE 'B' _____ 0 · 50

CARBONIFEROUS LIMESTONE _____ 0 · 30

DOLOMITIC LIMESTONE _____ 0 · 66

L. ESTURINE LIMESTONE _____ 0 · 63

FIG. 1. Surfacing trials—SFC values.

Surface Dressing Association.[3] A comprehensive manual is currently being prepared by TRRL.

(d) The improvement of riding quality, elimination of spray hazard and environmental nuisance can be achieved by the removal of surfacing by heating and planing, and replacement by a thin wearing course or mix-in-place techniques. It should be emphasised that all these techniques are of minor structural significance and so merely serve to delay deterioration.

The structural deterioration of a pavement in service is continuous and is accompanied by rising maintenance costs so that eventually pavement strengthening by overlaying, partial or total reconstruction, is required. To summarise, pavement maintenance is carried out for the following reasons:

(1) to remedy inadequate structural capacity by strengthening to increase the traffic bearing capacity;

(2) to remedy the level of surface to the road user in terms of riding comfort by resurfacing or mix-in-place;

(3) to counter structural distress or deterioration by patching and/or surface dressing;

(4) to improve the level of safety by resurfacing or mix-in-place to deal with wheel track rutting, and by surface dressing to improve skid resistance;

(5) to counter environmental nuisance, such as that produced by an uneven surface, by thin wearing courses or mix-in-place applications;

(6) to counter unacceptable road user costs and/or unacceptable maintenance costs.

Given the current restrictions on maintenance expenditure and the predicted future levels[4] coupled with the large price increases of tar and bitumen binders, together with the haulage costs for all maintenance activities, it is imperative that economically effective methods are used to determine when pavement maintenance should be executed, the type and the extent of the treatment. Furthermore, pavement maintenance must be considered in terms of an authority's highway network, the purpose it serves, and the resource constraints.

All of this demands a systematic approach embracing the processes applicable to the formulation of pavement maintenance programmes so that they are applied in a way which recognises their inter-relationship and optimises their potential contribution to economically effective decision making.

HISTORICAL REVIEW

Until recently, decisions on pavement maintenance including strengthening have depended solely on the experienced subjective judgement of engineers in the field, responsible for the maintenance of all types of roads in an area in extent ranging from less than 100 miles of town roads to 1000 miles of mainly rural highways. Observing road condition frequently as they travel around their area such engineers and their technical support have acquired considerable knowledge of pavement behaviour and the effect of various treatments. Furthermore, they are sensitive to local demand, both political and social, and therefore their input to the decision-making process will remain an essential element.

The transition to a more objective approach to pavement maintenance in the UK is primarily attributable to a committee jointly established by central government and the local authority associations in 1967 under the chairmanship of Dr A. H. Marshall, Director of the Institute of Local

Government Studies, University of Birmingham. The report of the Committee on Highway Maintenance was published in 1970[5] and is commonly known as the Marshall Report. Covering the whole subject of highway maintenance it contains recommendations for future practice, reasons why there should be a change in practice, and outlines implementable processes.

Research carried out for the Marshall Committee established that the subjective judgement of maintenance engineers was far from consistent. In order to promote a consistent approach to the selection of road sections for treatment the Committee recommended a set of initial standards. The standards concerned with pavement maintenance are primarily based on percentage rates of deterioration, levels of SFC, depths of standing water, amounts of deformation, and surface irregularity.[6] These initial standards were based on the judgement of a panel of experienced engineers.

Research for the Marshall Committee also established that there was a lack of rational priority selection between works of pavement maintenance particularly for road strengthening, and so the Committee recommended the use of maintenance rating systems as the basis of regular documented inspections of a highway authority's road network and that to enable decisions on the relative value of competing projects and between a choice of treatments, economic assessments should be used.[7]

The Marshall Report also contains other recommendations affecting pavement maintenance concerned with work planning, plant control and utilisation.[8] The Marshall standards were intended as targets against which achievement could be adjudged and which in conjunction with recommendations on the desirable proportion of spending between the main areas of maintenance and on the adoption of the maintenance rating system expenditure priorities could be assessed, thus securing better value for money from existing funds. It was recognised that the standards were primarily based upon subjective judgement and the Committee recommended the use and development of apparatus for measuring the condition of roads.[9]

The Marshall Report also expresses the Committee's concern about the inadequacy of available data, an aspect that was particularly apparent to the research team in its efforts to analyse and compare maintenance costs, practices, etc. of highway authorities.[10]

Since the publication of the Marshall Report a considerable amount of research has been carried out jointly and individually by TRRL and highway authorities in furtherance of the recommendations in the report. Some of these research projects have now produced implementable systems and techniques whilst others are approaching the report stage. Specifically the following relate to pavement maintenance:

(1) Surface dressing manual;
(2) Review of standards, engineering and economic levels;
(3) Maintenance rating systems;
(4) Techniques, organisation, costs of overlays, reconstruction;
(5) Techniques, organisation, costs of patching and the reinstatement of road openings;
(6) Development of measuring equipment.

Reference will be made to some of these projects and their findings in the detailed discussion but certainly a stage has been reached in the development of pavement maintenance management where a broad decision framework can be produced which can accept currently available procedures and those that seem likely to become available in the comparatively near future enabling the production of a pavement maintenance strategy.

DECISION FRAMEWORK FOR A PAVEMENT MAINTENANCE STRATEGY

A highway authority must have regard to the needs of the entire highway network under its jurisdiction. Decision making at the network level is concerned with the selection of individual sections of road for treatment in accordance with the availability of funds and is therefore a matter of the assignment of priorities related to need. Decision making for individual projects may take into account such criteria as cost, safety, level of service, load carrying ability, disruption to traffic during road works, environmental disturbance during road works, and aesthetics. The criteria for the technique and procedures to be used in order to arrive at the stage where such decisions can be taken should also be considered. Such criteria could be concerned with the following.

(a) Uniform condition survey techniques and procedures
In considering the application of survey techniques and procedures it must be recognised that because of financial constraints the possibility of anticipating major pavement expenditure on a road as it deteriorates towards structural failure by strengthening with an overlay before marked signs of distress appear is in practice seldom if ever realisable. It may

therefore be sensible to consider whether the first input into a process should not be a report of obvious distress to be followed by a detailed condition survey.

(*b*) *Data storage and retrieval systems*
Such systems should provide for the scanning of information of pavement history, construction details, quality control data, routine maintenance, non-routine repairs, and the reinstatement of road openings. Such a road information system should also incorporate any significant environmental factors, ecological characteristics, and traffic data.

(*c*) *Intervention levels*
Probably the most critical area in pavement maintenance. There can be a

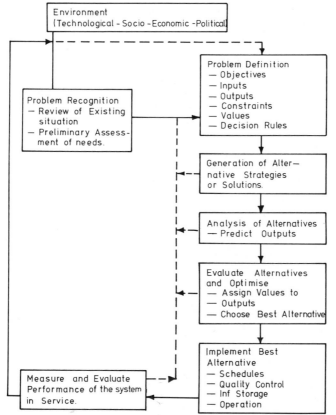

FIG. 2. Phases and components of systems method.

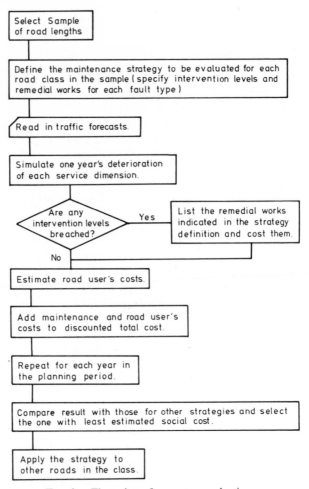

FIG. 3.   Flow chart for strategy selection.

variety of intervention levels for different states of pavement condition such
as those for legal liability, public acceptability, optimum economy, etc.
There is a need to define criteria which should ideally encompass user costs
as well as the economics of maintaining the pavement.

(*d*) *Predictive capability*
The repeated monitoring of road condition, etc. and the handling of data
should be aimed at the development of a predictive capability so as to be

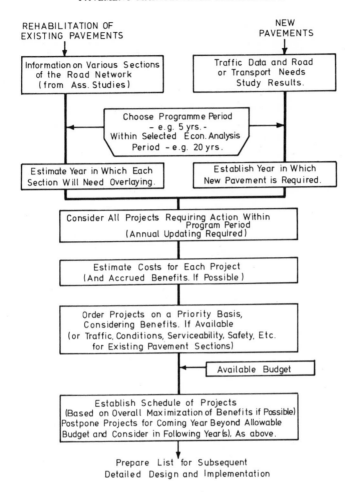

FIG. 4.   Steps in determining pavement investments over a chosen programme
period.

able to forecast the likely performance of a pavement on the basis of the
input data, and thus to predict the likely funding necessary for various
levels of pavement maintenance.

(e) Strategy
From the foregoing discussion it will be apparent that a decision framework
should provide for the disciplined development of an objective maintenance

strategy which encompasses currently available techniques and procedures and will allow the incorporation of those likely to be available in the reasonably near future. A system approach provides a suitable design format and has been adopted by several researchers.

Haas[11] has defined the phases and components as shown in Fig. 2. Beattie[12] has developed a system for producing an optimum pavement maintenance strategy on a random sample basis as shown in Fig. 3. This is an interesting approach but it is not currently implementable. In

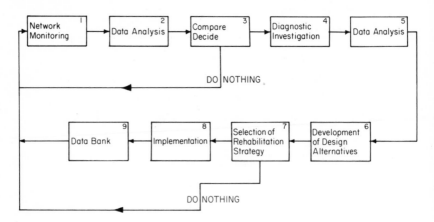

FIG. 5. Framework for pavement rehabilitation.

conjunction with information from a national random sample condition survey being carried out annually for the Standing Committee on Highway Maintenance it may well be developed as a means by which the national expenditure necessary for specific levels of pavement maintenance can be estimated.

An OECD Road Research Group [13] has defined steps in determining pavement investments over a chosen programme period as shown in Fig. 4, but this is too broad-brush an illustration for practical application. Other frameworks have been postulated but for practical application and development using the current and foreseeable techniques that originally were put forward by L. G. Byrd and F. N. Finn[14] as shown in Fig. 5 has much to commend it as a starting point for development. This format has been used to produce the framework shown in Fig. 6 which will be used as the basis for detailed consideration of the various elements which go towards producing a pavement maintenance programme. The framework

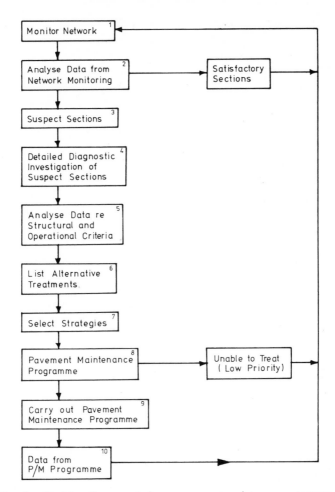

FIG. 6. Decision framework for a pavement maintenance strategy.

will be considered stage by stage with reference to objectives, techniques, procedures, and future research and development requirements.

COLLECTION OF DATA—MONITOR NETWORK

The objective of network monitoring is to provide basic, relevant, reliable information about past and present pavement performance. The execution of network monitoring comprises a number of activities involving various techniques and procedures. The activities are:

(a) condition survey;
(b) maintenance and operating costs;
(c) user costs;
(d) accident records;
(e) operational and environmental conditions.

(a) Condition Survey
The output from a condition survey should describe pavement condition at the time that the survey is undertaken. From the results of successive surveys a rate of change in conditions concerning a number of factors can be deduced. Information collated on distress must relate to some expression of performance so that comparisons can be made between different sections of road over given lengths of time and between time intervals, e.g. a time frequency for a specific section which will, for example, provide information on different types of treatment. The range of data collation that can be incorporated in a complete condition survey can be described as:

(i)   profile;
(ii)   physical distress;
(iii) strength or structural capacity;
(iv)   skid resistance.

(*i*) *Profile*
The collation of road profile data must incorporate a detailed inventory of highway dimensions including such features as the width of carriageway, footway and roadside verges, location and types of drainage, carriageway markings, physical features, pavement types and thickness, and all other features to provide a complete record of information. To collect this information for a complete highway network is a slow, laborious, labour intensive process. The processing can be expedited by survey teams inputting information direct onto computer forms, and the collation of inventory data can be combined with the collation of that on visually apparent distress.

The HIGHWAYMAN inventory system used by West Sussex County Council has been described by Garnett.[15]

It may be that in the future the process can be considerably speeded up by the development of photo-logging techniques. Although this is not common practice in the UK, information can also be collated on horizontal and vertical alignments and the surface irregularity of the pavement, e.g. riding quality. A 'Mobile Road Survey System' has been developed by FFV-U Sweden in close cooperation with the National Swedish Road Administration for the collection of road data for their Road Data Bank which is under development. The mobile system automatically measures the horizontal and vertical road alignment by the use of a gyro system and a data logging system triggered by a road distance measurement function. Data is recorded on punched paper tape and computer processed. The instruments are mounted on a four-wheel drive Chevrolet Chevy Suburban. A similar vehicle has been developed in France by the Laboratoire Central des Points et Chausees.

The standard method of measuring the surface irregularity of roads is through the use of a Bump Integrator. This machine is designed to measure the vertical movement of a single wheel relative to its mounting frame as it travels over the road at a uniform speed. The mounting and clamping of the wheel are standardised so that measurements obtained are consistent and the irregularity measurement obtained per section of road is a measure of the surface standard of the road. The Bump Integrator used in the UK is a single-wheel trailer designed by the TRRL. The machine is towed over a measured distance at a constant speed of 20 miles h^{-1} and the integrated upward movement of the wheel, relative to the chassis, is recorded. This movement, divided by the distance travelled, gives an 'Index of Irregularity' providing an objective assessment of the surface of the road. There is considerable doubt whether Bump Integrator values are a reliable measure of riding quality.

TRRL have developed a new longitudinal road profilometer and a prototype device using contact lens measuring techniques has been constructed. It is claimed that accurate profile recordings can be made at high speed.[16]

A variety of equipment has been developed and is in use in Europe and North America[13] of which the best known are the AASHO slope profilometer, the CHLOE profilometer, the PCA Road Meter, and the Mays Ride Meter.

It will be appreciated that a complete physical inventory of a road network is a once for all time operation providing that there are adequate arrangements for updating.

(ii) Physical Distress
The Marshall Committee recommended that highway authorities should

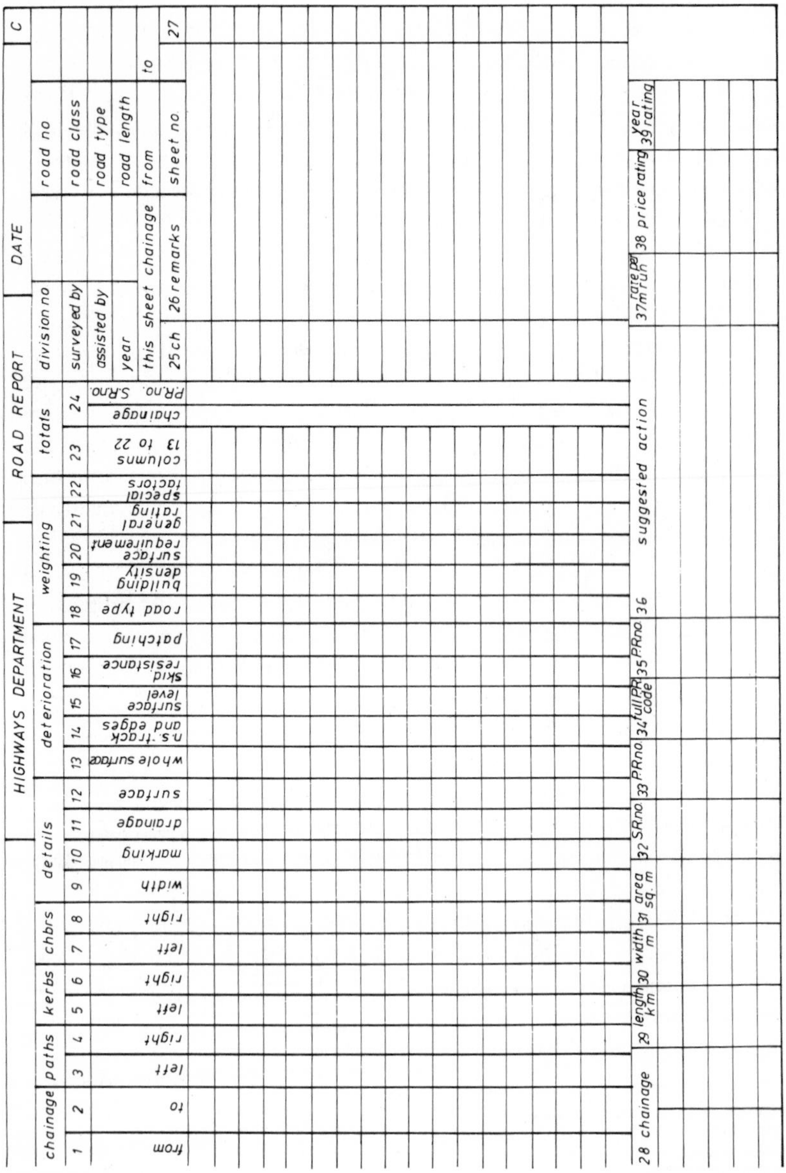

FIG. 7. Field assessment form—Marshall Rating system.

use a maintenance rating system as the basis of a regular documented condition assessment of their roads. The Marshall Report contains a maintenance rating system[17] which is based on the sufficiency rating system used in the USA. The system is based on visual inspection with points allocated to a range of defects comprising deterioration over the whole surface or in the wheel tracks, or at the edges, deformation of the carriageway, the need for patching, the camber, surface irregularity, skidding resistance, condition of joints (concrete roads), drainage, condition of road markings, kerbs, footways, and of existing patching.

The field assessment point rating relates to specific criteria or standards and for this purpose the Marshall standards are used since the relative condition of roads is the critical factor. An inspection sheet is shown in Fig. 7. The points given to the various defects are subsequently weighted and each assessed aspect adjudged critical or satisfactory. A computer program enables rapid processing of field assessments. This system has the defect that the results primarily depend upon an inspector's subjective visual assessment and if more than one inspector is used to survey a network the reliability of the information is further diminished. However, the Marshall Rating system is quick and can be used to provide a 'global' condition assessment of a highway network indicating which road sections of that network are in a suspect condition.

In the UK two condition assessment systems have been developed which minimise subjective judgement and optimise an objective, numerate, quantitative approach. In both systems the measured condition of defects such as the depth of wheel track rutting is related to standard criteria which are developments of the Marshall Standards. Both systems incorporate computer processing and have a variety of outputs portraying road conditions and priorities for remedial treatment.

The MARCH system: This system was developed by a group of engineers from the major cities in the UK. The condition data is collected by totals of defects, e.g. length, area, number within a specified length of road, so that the precise location of individual defective lengths, areas or units making up the totals within the specified 'treatment length', is not known. The treatment or maintenance lengths can vary up to 999 m but are usually 500 m.

The data is collected in a form from which the computer input can be directly punched. The output comprises priority lists of maintenance lengths and treatments required, based upon the worst defect present, and lists of maintenance lengths with full assessment and inventory data. The system also provides a costing option.

An Inspection Sheet is shown in Fig. 8 and the system outline in Fig. 9. The system is fully described in a User Manual[18] and practical experience in operation and use of output has been described by J. A. Cowley and J. P. Robinson.[19]

The CHART system: This system was developed by the TRRL/Local Highway Authorities' joint working party on the economics of highway maintenance. In principle it is similar to the MARCH system but the defects data is located by distance measurement along a road so that the location of each defect is known. The field inspection measurement and recording of defects covers:

> For carriageways: surface failure; structural failure including failure at the edges as revealed by deformation and cracking; unacceptable transverse slope (camber).
>
> For footways and kerbs: surface failure; deterioration of kerbs; unacceptable kerb upstand; lack of kerbs.
>
> For drainage: unacceptable retention of water on the carriageway surface.

The output includes a 'map' of all roads inspected showing the location of defects and features along the road, histograms of the combined ratings for all defects present, lists showing critical sub-sections, i.e. 100 m lengths and individual defect and treatment length lists in order of priority of need for treatment. The system has been fully described and illustrated in a published report[20] and operational experience has been described by G. M. Senior.[21]

Detailed visual assessment systems such as CHART or MARCH provide a comprehensive measured distress record but both are very slow in collecting information and over a large network are resource expensive. According to the MARCH user manual a Field Assessment Team of 2/3 technicians can achieve a rate of inspection in rural areas of 8 km day^{-1} and in 'built-up' areas of 6 km day^{-1}. The TRRL CHART report for a similar assessment team gives rates of inspection ranging from below 1 km day^{-1} on very important urban trunk roads to 8–10 km day^{-1} on rural minor roads. Thus both systems have the following drawbacks:

> (a)   a very long procedure involving substantial manpower;

(b)   a need for qualified inspectors to minimise the human factor in interpreting road conditions.

Therefore if a comprehensive approach is adopted for the determination of pavement needs as exemplified by the decision framework it may be that neither CHART nor MARCH are appropriate for monitoring a large network and are more effectively employed at the detailed diagnostic stage. Although the Marshall rating system is not so objective it is quick and will provide a 'global' picture of the network which may be sufficient for monitoring a large network. However, there are developments overseas which could provide a more accurate rapid assessment as required for network monitoring. These are related to the photographic inventory techniques used in the USA and Canada.[22]

In France a photographic recorder (GERPHO) has been developed which provides a continuous picture of the road surface at a scale of 1:200 showing surface damage and longitudinal deformation which can be analysed and the percentage of damaged surface calculated.[23] Recording is carried out at between 40 and 60 km h^{-1}. Wheel track rutting cannot be recorded by the GERPHO process but an instrument for automatically measuring rut depth is used in the Netherlands. Rut depth is recorded continuously in the towing vehicle at 50 km h^{-1}.[24]

(iii) Strength or Structural Capacity
In the UK the Benkelman Beam and the Lacroix Deflectograph are commonly used to provide a measure of structural capacity (see Chapter 4). Use of the Benkelman Beam is very slow and this is definitely not applicable to network condition monitoring. The Deflectograph could be used for the routine measurement of a network but considering the capital investment and operational cost of the machine, together with the short season over which it can reliably operate, it would seem more appropriate to concentrate its use at the diagnostic stage. Discussion of the Deflectograph is therefore incorporated in that on the diagnostic stage of the framework.

(iv) Skid Resistance
In the UK (as mentioned in ref. 37) the TRRL Pendulum Skid Tester is almost universally in use by highway authorities to measure skid resistance at suspect sites such as where accident records indicate skidding as a contributory factor. However, the machine only provides a spot recording and is not appropriate to the routine monitoring of a highway network.

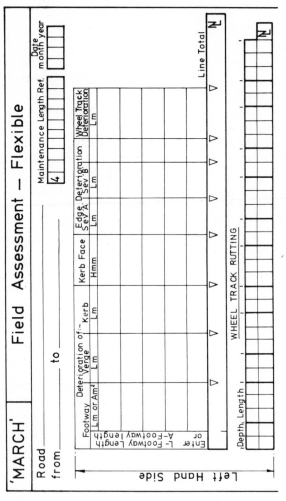

FIG. 8.   Field assessment form—MARCH Rating system.

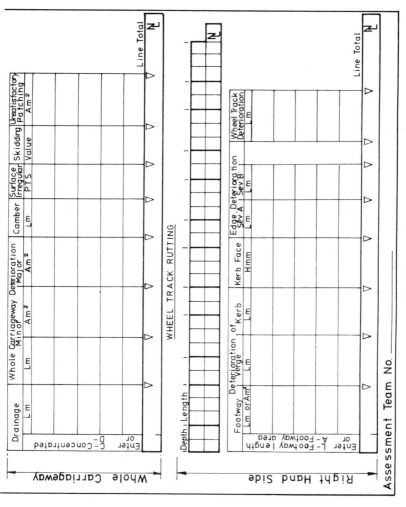

Fig. 8.—contd.

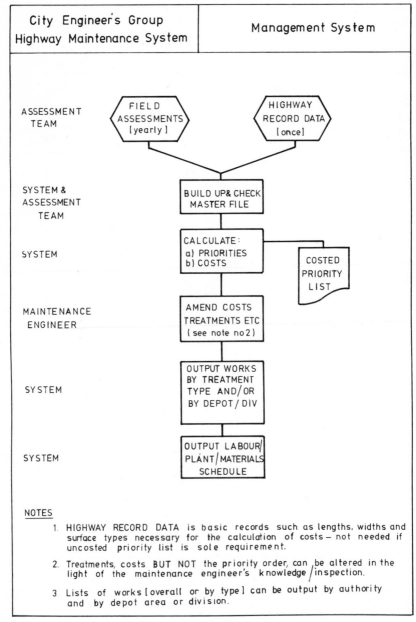

City Engineer's Group Highway Maintenance System	Management System

ASSESSMENT TEAM
FIELD ASSESSMENTS [yearly] HIGHWAY RECORD DATA [once]

SYSTEM & ASSESSMENT TEAM
BUILD UP & CHECK MASTER FILE

SYSTEM
CALCULATE:
a) PRIORITIES
b) COSTS

COSTED PRIORITY LIST

MAINTENANCE ENGINEER
AMEND COSTS TREATMENTS ETC (see note no 2)

SYSTEM
OUTPUT WORKS BY TREATMENT TYPE AND/OR BY DEPOT / DIV

SYSTEM
OUTPUT LABOUR/PLANT/MATERIALS SCHEDULE

NOTES

1. HIGHWAY RECORD DATA is basic records such as lengths, widths and surface types necessary for the calculation of costs — not needed if uncosted priority list is sole requirement.

2. Treatments, costs BUT NOT the priority order, can be altered in the light of the maintenance engineer's knowledge/inspection.

3. Lists of works [overall or by type] can be output by authority and by depot area or division.

FIG. 9. System outline—MARCH Rating system.

The SCRIM machine was developed by TRRL for the routine testing of a highway network, the name being a mnemonic for Sideway Force Coefficient Routine Investigation Machine. Fundamentally the machine is a lorry mounted water tank with a test wheel mounted between the front and rear wheels so as to measure skid resistance in the nearside wheel track. It records the SFC and gives a mean reading for every 10 m (or 5 or 20 m) length of road. 'Events' can be recorded on the print-out such as a change in surfacing material. Test speeds range from 15 to 100 km h^{-1}. The machine is readily available for purchase or hire in the UK. The use of a SCRIM machine to monitor the highway network of the Greater London Council has been described by L. W. Hatherley.[25]

In considering the techniques and procedures to be incorporated in the condition survey part of network monitoring it should be appreciated that the philosophy of a decision framework, if it is to be used for the systematic formulation of both annual and long term pavement maintenance programmes, must be on the basis of speed, reliability and cost.

It may be that random sampling can be used to establish the overall condition and rate of deterioration of a network, and in fact a national survey is being conducted under the auspices of the Standing Committee on Highway Maintenance. Such a survey could be used to assess the financial implications of maintaining a network to various levels but it will not reveal which sections of road in a network need treatment or merit detailed investigation.

The requirement is to obtain an overall condition picture of a network quickly that will highlight suspect lengths for more detailed investigation at a later stage but will nevertheless provide a realistic overview of the requirement for an annual pavement maintenance programme, and from the interpretation of successive surveys permit an assessment of the longer term requirements. Therefore with the currently available UK techniques and procedures a Network Monitoring Condition Survey could comprise:
—Road Inventory with routine update.
—Condition assessment by Marshall Rating System.
—SCRIM survey.

(b) Maintenance and Operating Costs
Cost is critical in terms of the use of resources—time, equipment, personnel. However, at the network monitoring stage the prime interest is in the collation of cost records for subsequent cost-benefit and cost-effectiveness analysis. Maintenance costs can be collated in two forms: Unit costs and costs per length of road.

DEPARTMENT OF THE ENVIRONMENT
TR 121A (Revise)
MOTORWAY AND TRUNK ROAD MAINTENANCE
Works and Expenditure for Year Ending ⎯⎯⎯⎯⎯⎯⎯ 19
Agent Authority ⎯⎯⎯⎯⎯⎯⎯⎯⎯⎯⎯⎯⎯⎯⎯⎯⎯⎯⎯

Code no. 1	Operation 2	Estimated cost £ 3	Cost approved by RC (R & T) £ 4	Actual cost £ 5
1	Reconstruction, including haunching and other ancillary works (except addition of new kerbing)			
2	Overlay, including all ancillary works (except addition of new kerbing)			
3	Resurfacing to existing levels (except where part of reconstruction) including all ancillary works (except addition of new kerbing)			
4	Surface Dressing (inclusive of patching or regulation; and see item 9)			
5	Patching flexible roads (and other minor ad hoc repairs)			
6	Patching concrete roads (sealing and repairs to slabs)			
7	Bridges, (including painting) and culverts over 1·5 metres			
8	Subways, retaining walls and other structures			
9	Special anti-skid treatment			
10	Footways and cycle tracks (including ancillary works)			
11	Provision of new kerbs where none previously existed			
12	Raising or replacing existing kerbs			
13	Remedial earthworks, embankments and cuttings			
14	Drainage, including culverts under 1·5 metres but excluding gully emptying			

Signature of County Surveyor   ....
Date   ....
Signature of RC (R & T)   ....
Date   ....

Note: Codes 1–14. The operations should be listed on p. 2 where the expenditure on a given item at one location exceeds £5000.

FIG. 10.   Accounting heads—motorway and trunk road maintenance.

Road no. _____

No. of Traffic Lanes	S2L	S3L	D2L	D3L	D4L	Total
Agency Length						

Council Ref. ....

Department Ref......................

Code no. 6	Operation 7	Estimated cost £ 8	Cost approved by RC (R & T) £ 9	Actual cost £ 10
15	Verge maintenance (including grass cutting, siding, and spraying for weed control)			
16	Hedge and tree maintenance			
17	Road markings and reflector studs (including provision of new)			
18	Gully emptying			
19	Safety Fences (including provision)			
20	Boundary fences (including provision)			
21	Pedestrian guard rails (including provision)			
22	Pedestrian crossings and furniture (including provision and energy)			
23	Traffic lights (excluding expenditure on new sites but including area control costs and energy costs)			
24	Traffic signs, bollards, direction signs (to include motorway surveillance systems, telephones, warning signs and their lighting cleaning, etc; and energy costs)			
25	Sweeping, cleansing etc. including motorway patrols			
26	Precautionary salting (give quantity of salt used on page 2)			
27	Snow clearing, including erection and removal of snow fences			
28	Motorway compounds structural maintenance costs (details on page 2)			
29	Under-road heating (including provision and energy)			
30	Motorway Staff Costs			
31	Technical surveys			
32	Other items (details on page 2)			
	TOTAL ITEMS 1–32			
	Administrative Allowance			
	GRAND TOTAL			

FIG. 10.—contd.

The Marshall Report recommended seventeen functional accounting heads for maintenance costing throughout the UK and with modifications these have been adopted as shown in Fig. 10. The accounting heads can be sub-divided so as to provide unit costs for all types of maintenance. For example the cost per square metre of a specific thickness and type of surfacing. Such costing is commonly carried out by highway authorities in the UK. The costs can be used for initial programme estimates and for management cost control. However, they only represent average costs for the various activities over a network and thus do not permit comparative analysis between sections of road or between types of treatment. They do not enable the identification of unacceptable routine maintenance costs which as previously described could be a criteria for treatment, nor do they permit the analysis of previous maintenance decisions. For these purposes it is necessary that actual expenditure is recorded under each operation code against each section of road. Routine maintenance activities must be included so that the 'do nothing' alternative can be evaluated.

Although it is not currently common practice by highway authorities in the UK there seems to be no fundamental reason why there cannot be costing to road section as well as the customary unit costing. Direct operating costs include fuel, maintenance, and wear and tear depreciation, but exclude insurance, time related depreciation, annual taxes, and other costs which do not vary with vehicle usage. Although the direct costs can be estimated by reference to existing cost data, experience in the UK is that the relationship between standards of maintenance and operating costs on surfaced roads is weak. It has been found that vehicle operating costs will only react to maintenance standards when these change sufficiently to cause vehicle speed to change, and this is only likely to occur on unsurfaced or badly damaged roads. Direct operating costs can therefore be ignored as far as practice in the UK is concerned although they can have considerable bearing elsewhere.

(c) User Costs

These are concerned with time and the value placed by the user on riding comfort. Separate values of time can be calculated for working time (based on road users' wage rates) and non-working time. There is a Department of Transport method for calculating these values[26] but the evaluation of travel time is more applicable to the cost-benefit analysis of road improvements and is seldom applicable to maintenance decisions. A case could arise though where, for example, the strengthening of a weight restricted road could reduce journey time. Delay costs are certainly applicable since the type of treatment and method of operation can have a significant effect upon traffic delays. Currently, however, information applicable to the UK is lacking although there is a long term TRRL research programme. However, Karen and Haas have shown that such costs can affect the choice of treatment.[27]

(d) Accident Records

The collation of accident records is an essential part of network monitoring. In the UK all personal injury accidents are reported and these are recorded in a standard form which permits a variety of analysis. For example the number and location of accidents involving skidding is obviously an important indicator of the need for anti-skid treatment such as surface dressing. Accident costs are an important factor in economic analysis and the Department of Transport produces a regularly updated actuarial value for the various types of accidents including loss of wages, damage to property, police and hospital costs. Research has established a relationship between the occurrence of injury and non-injury accidents so that the latter can be taken into account.[28] Long term accident analysis could be used to determine relationships with the quality of maintenance.

(e) Operational and Environmental Conditions

Traffic

In assessing the future life of a pavement and in determining strengthening requirements the most important factor is the magnitude of vehicle axle loads.

Overlay design and future life estimation using the method produced in the TRRL Report LR 571[29] and discussed fully in Chapter 4 based upon deflection measurement depends upon the standard axle load concept and for this to be accurately applied traffic axle load distribution, past, present and future, must be known.

Unfortunately the information commonly collated by highway authorities is concerned with traffic volumes and in some instances PCU figures are available. Consequently the conversion factors quoted in Road Note 29[30] have to be used. Peattie[31] has drawn attention to these deficiencies and to the likely effects of changes in the maximum permitted axle load. Hill and Thorpe[32] have maintained that the equality of damaging power assumed in Report LR 571 and Road Note 29 in contra-flow traffic conditions can be alarmingly misleading. Therefore what is required is an efficient and quick method of determining axle loads that can be used for routine network monitoring.

A portable axle (or wheel) weighing apparatus has been developed by the Overseas Unit of the Transport and Road Research Laboratory which could be used on a sampling basis.[33] Records of traffic flows are an essential input for specifying surface treatment and in assessing rates of deterioration. The development of traffic models enables the flow on any part of a network to be reliably estimated.

Climate
It may well be that rainfall and temperature records would prove useful in long term condition analysis although in a temperate climate only very exceptional conditions appear to have substantial effects upon the lives of treatments.

Geography
In certain areas the type of terrain is relevant to the pavement maintenance strategy and must be taken into account.

Noise
Potential noise problems may be a criteria that should be recorded. In some localities the noise may exclude the use of certain types of treatment or will determine the service level. Empty lorries on an uneven surface in a residential area can create considerable disturbance so that political pressure may determine far less surface irregularity than would otherwise be regarded as appropriate for intervention.

Roadside Hazards
These will be recorded in the road inventory.

Cultural Environment
The surroundings contiguous to the highway could well be relevant to a selection of treatment and may in fact rule out specific choices. The choices of treatment can be particularly relevant to conservation areas where the requirement may be for the highway to be in harmony with the surrounding fabric.

To summarise, the foregoing discussion has been concerned with the identification of factors relevant to the routine network monitoring of pavements. Quite obviously a considerable volume of data could be collected under the guise of network monitoring but the objective of basic, relevant, reliable information should not be overlooked. Time and resources are always limited so that although a considerable volume of data could be collected there must be rigorous control of what and how much information is really needed at this stage.

ANALYSIS OF DATA

In order to handle the various types of information collected under network monitoring an Information/Data Base system is required. The County Surveyors' Society System TARA[34] provides a system for establishing throughout a road network a series of node (junction) and link locations from which uniquely numbered sections can be derived in accordance with the road categorisation. Thus for any section or 'treatment length' the relevant array of information can be retrieved. The information collected under Network Monitoring can all be related to the links and sections of this register.

The objective at this stage of the decision making process is to estimate present and future levels of performance and to make preliminary costings assuming that no treatment is programmed or implemented, i.e. the 'do nothing' situation.

It is necessary to define the type of analysis required for a *preliminary* decision on rehabilitation treatment. There are three prime considerations for analysis at this stage.

(1) *Performance*
The factors considered in assessing pavement performance have been discussed and the purpose at this stage is to make a forecast of deterioration.

Clearly the use of limiting criteria or intervention levels embracing levels of service enters into this as do also the confidence intervals for prediction in terms of time and condition. As the years go by, repeated network monitoring analysis of the pavements deteriorating condition will enable more confident predictions on a condition assessment versus time basis to be made, and this will permit longer term forward programming.

(2) *Cost Prediction*
The objective is to predict the cost of doing or not doing rehabilitation. Ideally such costs would be the total of pavement maintenance and user costs but, as previously discussed, inclusion of the latter is not currently

practical. Cost predictions should also incorporate maintenance costs after the completion of treatment.

In time, after repeated monitoring, it would be possible to identify the influence of pavement maintenance decisions such as the amount of strengthening and specification of material upon performance and cost.

(3) Environmental Impact/Socio-Political Conditions

This is a vague area requiring a great deal of subjective judgement where engineering management experience is critical. It must be considered and analysis made since these influences can affect both the decision to treat and the type of treatment.

A preliminary decision based on the results of network monitoring and data analysis can be made with the objective of determining whether some form of rehabilitation *might* be required. The initial examination made at this stage must be on the basis of comparing a series of broad decision criteria against the output of the data analysis, e.g. performance standards, cost limits, safety, environmental impact of not correcting condition, socio-economic considerations. At this stage a 'do nothing' alternative is brought into play and in that case road sections are returned to network monitoring.

The situation at the end of this stage is that a 'coarse sieve' has been used over the road network and suspect sections have been identified for closer examination.

INVESTIGATION OF SUSPECT SECTIONS

The purpose of the diagnostic investigation is to obtain the detailed information necessary for the evaluation of various pavement maintenance strategies. In some respects this investigation is similar to Network Monitoring in that condition data is required. However, the nature of the survey is significantly different from that for network monitoring in that far more detailed study is required. The identification of suspect sections via the coarse sieve of network monitoring enables, at this stage, the cost-effective concentration of processes which are demanding financially and in their use of skilled resources.

The determination of the cause of pavement deterioration is important in the collation of data for use in producing alternative pavement maintenance strategies. It is necessary to discover whether factors are present which demand treatment other than to the pavement itself such as inadequate drainage. A measurements programme is required which will produce detailed information on condition, strength, construction, safety and relevant environment condition so as to provide the complete information package necessary to meet the objective.

Condition

A very detailed assessment of condition can be obtained using the CHART or MARCH systems previously described. Both the computer based systems provide priority rankings for treatment based on the comprehensive measurement of visible deterioration together with indications of the corrective treatment required.

Strength

A deflectograph survey of the suspect sections will provide a measure of their structural capacity.

This method is now used by several highway authorities in the UK and the machine is generally available for purchase and hire.

Deflectograph surveys of trunk roads for rehabilitation programming are now required by the Department of Transport.[35] Assessment of performance and overlay design is discussed in Chapter 4 and suffice it to say in this discussion that TRRL in Report LR 571 have produced criteria for relating deflection measurements to pavement maintenance and overlay design and that, as indicated in the paper by Hill and Thorpe,[32] these criteria have been successfully extended to cover a variety of carriageway construction including undesigned pavements.

It is understood that revised and extended recommendations are to be published by TRRL in the near future and these will no doubt reflect the approach outlined by Lister and Kennedy.[36] It should be appreciated that many well trafficked roads are undesigned or successive treatments have rendered the design details of no use in considering overlay design. Furthermore, even where the pavement has not been treated since the initial construction, coring has revealed that the actual thicknesses of construction materials can vary markedly from that shown on the design drawings. Therefore the deflectograph survey should be backed up by carriageway coring to ensure that accurate information about the existing road structure is available, e.g. thickness and type of bituminous materials, state of compaction or densification, oxidation or stripping of binder, cause of localised failure.

Additionally the state of the sub-grade and water table levels often require investigation by means of an auger survey in the adjacent roadside

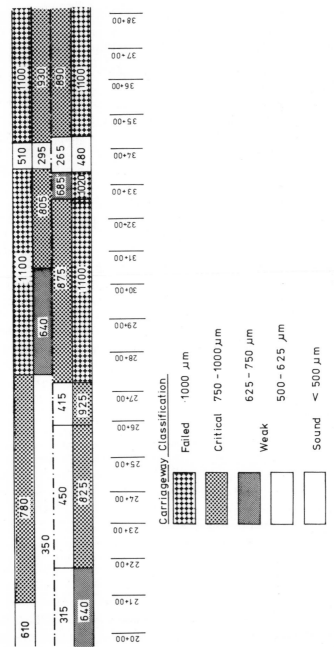

FIG. 11. Carriageway diagram—deflectograph survey.

verge. Improved drainage can be as effective as an overlay in restoring structural capacity or can reduce the amount of overlay required.

Permanent deformation will have been recorded as part of the CHART or MARCH survey. Often such deformation is caused by plastic flow of the wearing course or densification of open textured or single course/base course materials and not structural weakness. Authorities regularly carrying out deflectograph surveys have experienced several cases of carriageways of adequate stiffness but with high surface deformation. The need for traffic information to achieve accurate interpretation of deflectograph results has already been discussed.

From the processed deflectograph survey of a suspect section produced from the analysis of network monitoring a diagram such as shown in Fig. 11 can be produced. This is taken from an actual case where the results of visual assessment indicated a need to overlay the complete 1·8 km suspect section with an overlay of 100 mm thickness. The survey shows a change in stiffness not apparent from visual assessment so that for 0·7 km of carriageway only 50 mm of overlay was required with 100 mm over the remaining 1·1 km. This is a substantial saving.

In fact an analysis of suspect sections recommended for overlay treatment on the sole basis of visual assessment will produce instances where no strengthening is required, where the indicated strengthening is excessive and also where the indicated strengthening is so inadequate that the overlay would be immediately overstressed and then the optimum benefit would not be obtained.

The deflectograph can also be used in the development of a surfacing policy by monitoring treated sections and thus determining the effect of pavement maintenance decisions in terms of the relative strengthening properties of different designs and thicknesses of bituminous materials.

The machine can also be used to assess the damage caused to the pavement by substantial road openings such as for main drainage schemes and by the diversionary routing of traffic arising from road closures.

Safety
Information on skid resistance for the suspect section will be available if a SCRIM survey has been carried out as part of network monitoring. Alternatively, where the combined MARCH/CHART and deflectograph surveys indicate that an overlay is not required, pendulum skid test measurements could be taken on those sections to determine whether the skid resistance is adequate.

Maintenance Cost
The maintenance costs for each of the suspect sections would be available from the analysis of network monitoring as previously discussed.

Accidents
The accident record for each of the suspect sections would be available from the analysis of network monitoring as previously discussed.

Operational and Environmental Conditions
The relevant operational and environmental conditions would be available from the analysis of network monitoring.

ALTERNATIVE TREATMENTS

Analyse Data—Structural and Operational Criteria
The objective at this stage is to analyse the array of information produced by the detailed diagnostic investigation of suspect sections so as to indicate the pavement maintenance required to remedy the defects of the pavement that have been diagnosed. The criteria listed in the Introduction to this chapter can be used to determine the broad nature of the required treatment. For example, is there a need to:

—Remedy inadequate structural capacity and/or increase traffic bearing capacity?
—Remedy the level of surface to the road user?
—Counter structural distress or deterioration?
—Improve the level of safety?
—Counter environmental nuisance?
—Counter unacceptable maintenance costs?

From an analysis on these lines for each of the suspect sections a detailed schedule can be produced of the specific requirements for treatment.

List Alternative Treatments
The objective is to develop and list alternative treatments which will meet the requirements indicated by the analysis of structural and operational criteria.

Alternative treatments can be listed for the dominant requirement of each suspect section. The broad alternatives that will be considered for any section are:

(i)   continue existing routine maintenance, i.e. postpone treatment;
(ii)   overlay, resurface or reconstruct—will increase structural capacity, improve riding quality, improve skid resistance;
(iii)   surface dress with or without pad coat, patching, etc.—will seal cracked pavements against ingress of water, improve skid resistance;
(iv)   strengthen base, sub-base or sub-grade by improved drainage;
(v)   reworking of in-place materials—will improve riding quality, counter environmental nuisance.

Thus for example, if the prime requirement is to strengthen, the alternative treatments listed can comprise:

(a)   overlay—thicknesses and types of material for desired life;
(b)   reconstruction—design thicknesses and specification of materials;
(c)   improved drainage—type and location;
(d)   full depth patching of weak areas, regulation course and resurface—patching method and material, material for regulating course thickness and type of wearing course;
(e)   full depth patching of weak areas and surface dress—patching method and material, type of surface dressing;
(f)   postpone treatment.

If riding quality or the removal of environmental nuisance is the dominant requirement the alternatives can comprise:

(a)   heat and plane to restore profile and resurface—depth of surface removal, thickness and type of wearing course;
(b)   regulating course and resurface—specification of regulating course, thickness and type of wearing course;
(c)   regulating course and surface dress—specification of regulating course—type of surface dressing;
(d)   rework in-place materials with or without additives and with or without additional wearing course or surface dressing—specification of in-place treatment, type and thickness of wearing course, type of surface dressing;
(e)   postpone treatment.

If improvement of the safety level is the prime consideration the alternatives can comprise:

(a) resurfacing with a friction course—thickness and specification;
(b) surface dressing—type of surface dressing;
(c) postpone treatment.

If the prime consideration is to counter unacceptable maintenance costs then virtually any one of the treatments previously listed could be considered.

The foregoing is only illustrative. There are a wide range of treatments and combinations of treatments which can be used to meet various requirements. However, in listing alternative treatments that are relevant to the previously defined needs of the sections under consideration, a certain amount of basic knowledge on the properties of materials and the specification of treatments is essential:

—Thicknesses and types of material to provide desired improvements in service level.
—Properties of materials, effect of time, temperature, fuel spillage, etc.
—Types of treatment that will provide desired skid resistance.
—Performance of aggregates for satisfactory skid resistance.

It will be appreciated that, in theory, a considerable list of alternative treatments can be produced, particularly if different specifications, types of aggregate and types of binder are considered. However, many alternatives can be excluded at the listing stage such as, for example, a thick overlay for a section in an urban area where surface levels adjacent to the carriageway will not permit. Furthermore, if the highway authority has evolved a surfacing policy, selection of appropriate treatments for consideration is greatly simplified since such a policy involves the identification of the most suitable materials available to the authority for the various treatments, i.e. wearing courses, base courses, surface dressings. The elements of a surfacing policy can be descirbed as:

(a) strengthening capabilities;
(b) skid resistance properties;
(c) expected lives of treatments;
(d) riding quality, noise, spray;
(e) initial cost, cost/life indices;
(f) aesthetic appeal.

Given that the required improvement in strength is known, the thickness

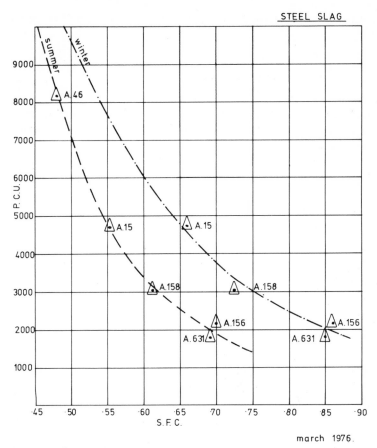

FIG. 12. Surfacing trials, SFC vs. PCUs—dense bituminous wearing course macadam.

and types of material that will give the desired improvement need to be identified and surfacing trials incorporating deflectograph monitoring can establish this information. Recent developments in overlay design are dealt with in Chapter 4 and the use of analytical methods in this context is interesting.

Given that the required skid resistance is known, it is necessary to identify which treatments will provide that skid resistance and which aggregates are satisfactory. The various factors affecting resistance to skidding are fully discussed by Lees.[37] Figure 12 shows the results of a typical surfacing trial for skid resistance using locally available aggregate. Trials can establish lives for surface dressings, wearing courses, and base courses for the particular condition in the area together with the performance of those materials in terms of riding quality, noise, and spray. The initial cost per square metre of treatment can be established by trials with records of actual rates of spread achieved. Cost/life indices can be produced for various treatments and where costs are equal the material which provides the better overall performance can be identified.

Finally for those cases where environmental considerations are critical the important factors of colour, texture, life, noise, and spray can be taken into account.

Thus the most appropriate alternative treatments can be selected for each road section under consideration.

Select Strategies

The objective is to provide from the list of alternative treatments an array of alternative strategies for evaluation. The criteria to be considered in the optimisation procedure can be expressed as:

(a) minimisation of expenditure;
(b) level of safety;
(c) serviceability to the user;
(d) load carrying capacity;
(e) rate of deterioration under traffic and environmental influences;
(f) disruption to traffic during treatment;
(g) disruption to adjoining properties, etc. during and after treatment;
(h) aesthetics.

It will be appreciated that the alternative treatments listed for each road section in themselves constitute the best available choice of their type in terms of these criteria for each road section. The end product from this stage is a choice of pavement maintenance programmes for all the sections under consideration. The inevitable consequence of trying to comply with the criteria is that they cannot all be achieved to an optimum degree so that any strategy selection will be a compromise. Choice depends upon the relative importance attached to the criteria for each road section in terms of route importance, locality, traffic and the availablility of funds. Economy must be of prime importance for, as discussed in the Introduction to this chapter, maintenance funds are severely restricted so there is very little possibility of sufficient funds being available to carry out a programme which incorporates the most desired treatment for each road section. Safety is a major requirement and serviceability over the life of the treatment should be within acceptable limits.

The provision of strength is bound to compete with the minimisation of expenditure so that critical risk assessments have to be made. Preventive overlays to strengthen pavements before they reach minimum levels of acceptability are seldom possible.

The minimisation of deterioration has been listed as a criteria because of its influence upon economic considerations in terms of strengthening and maintenance costs.

Generally the last three criteria are of lesser importance. However, cases can occur in specific localities where they can override economic considerations.

Since economy is of prime importance the production of alternative pavement strategies will primarily depend upon economic analysis and other influences will only have a marginal effect upon the alternative programmes. As previously discussed, the first essential for economic analysis is reliable cost data.

Unit costs should be available for each maintenance operation so that the cost of treatment can be estimated. Additionally, data should be available for the estimation of maintenance costs over the analysis period.

The drawback with unit costs is that they are essentially historical and therefore particularly unreliable in an inflationary period. Under the auspices of the TRRL/Highway Authorities' working party on maintenance a work study based computerised estimating system called RATE is being developed which will provide up to date estimates for pavement maintenance together with the associated resources of plant, labour, and materials and this is likely to be released in the near future. A detailed discussion of various methods of economic analysis can be found in the OECD document 'Road Strengthening.'[13] A comparatively simple system whereby projects can be ranked in order of desirability by means of an Expenditure Priority Index is described in Appendix 3 of the Marshall Report.

PAVEMENT MAINTENANCE PROGRAMME

At the end of the process of strategy selection the best strategy in terms of the method of economic analysis used can be selected to form the Pavement Maintenance Programme.

However, the maintenance manager may have to consider other factors as well as economics. For example, works programmed by other authorities may include major road openings which will shorten the lives of treatments. Therefore a less economic strategy than the optimum may have to be selected. Restrictions on funding will inevitably mean for sections of the lowest priority a decision to continue with routine maintenance, the 'do nothing' alternative and, in this event, the relevant data is returned to storage and the sections involved are reinstated in the network monitoring process. Having produced a Pavement Maintenance Programme complete with costs and resources it must be executed.

Although this chapter is not concerned with the processes involved in carrying out the various surface treatments but with the management of pavement maintenance, certain 'key areas' can be highlighted:

(a)   construction techniques;
(b)   traffic handling;
(c)   material selection and quality control;
(d)   accurate allocation and control of plant, labour, and material resources;
(e)   cost control;
(f)   environmental consideration during works.

The execution of the Pavement Maintenance Programme is by no means the end of the manager's interest. The effectiveness of the pavement maintenance decisions should be evaluated to assist the development of future criteria and this necessitates recording details of cost, quality, performance, subsequent cost of routine maintenance, and comparison with design expectations for the treated sections together with the details of specification for the treatment adopted.

CONCLUSION

The purpose of this chapter has been to describe a step-by-step approach for the management of pavement maintenance describing the various matters that have to be considered along the way. The advantages of such an approach can be described as:

—Efficient and effective use of available funds.
—Objective and consistent decisions on the execution of pavement maintenance.
—Better use of materials.

—Optimisation of pavement maintenance decisions in terms of cost, resources, social impact, etc.

—A reliable tool for the engineer to manage a highway network.

Although such a total approach is not yet in general use by highway authorities in the UK it is known that several are moving in that direction. Comprehensive Road Information Systems are being developed, Condition Assessment Systems are being used to determine need as are SCRIM and the Deflectograph.

In conclusion the economically effective management of Pavement Maintenance requires some means of assurance that the priorities for treatment are in the right order and that the right materials are put down in the right place at the right time. A system has been described whereby, using available techniques and processes and allowing for those that will possibly become available, that aim stands a reasonable chance of being achieved.

It must be finally emphasised that effective management predominantly depends upon the collation of reliable data.

REFERENCES

1. DEPARTMENT OF THE ENVIRONMENT. Preferred methods of construction, Part 1: Patching, HMSO, London, 1973.
2. TRANSPORT AND ROAD RESEARCH LABORATORY. Recommendations for road surface dressing, Road Note 39, HMSO, London, 1972.
3. Road Surface Dressing, (a pocket guide based on Road Note 39), Road Surface Dressing Association, London.
4. DEPARTMENT OF TRANSPORT. Transport policy, Cmnd 6836, HMSO, London, 1977.
5. Report of the Committee on Highway Maintenance, HMSO, London, 1970.
6. Report of the Committee on Highway Maintenance, Appendix 1, HMSO, London, 1970.
7. Report of the Committee on Highway Maintenance, Ch. 5, HMSO, London, 1970.
8. Report of the Committee on Highway Maintenance, Ch. 8, HMSO, London, 1970.
9. Report of the Committee on Highway Maintenance, Ch. 4, HMSO, London, 1970.
10. Report of the Committee on Highway Maintenance, Ch. 11, HMSO, London, 1970.
11. HAAS, R. Pavement design and management systems, Transportation Research Record 512, Transportation Research Board, Washington DC, 1974.
12. BEATTIE, R. *The Surveyor*, Sept., 1975.

13. ORGANISATION OF ECONOMIC CO-OPERATION AND DEVELOPMENT. *Road strengthening*, OECD, Paris, 1976.
14. TRANSPORTATION RESEARCH BOARD. Pavement rehabilitation: Proceedings of a workshop, Report No. FHWA-RD-74-60, Federal Highway Administration, Washington DC, 1974.
15. GARNETT, R. S. Collection of highway inventory data, Proc. of PTRC Summer Annual Meeting, 1977, PTRC (ERS), London.
16. TRANSPORT AND ROAD RESEARCH LABORATORY. High speed road profilometer, Report SR 182, HMSO, London, 1977.
17. Report of the Committee on Highway Maintenance: Appendix 2: Maintenance Rating System, HMSO, London, 1970.
18. MARCH Working Group. MARCH Highway Maintenance System: User Manual, West Midlands County Council, Birmingham, 1975.
19. COWLEY, J. A. and ROBINSON, J. P. Practical experience in the operation of Highway Maintenance Systems and the use of their output, Proc. of PTRC Summer Annual Meeting, 1977, PTRC (ERS), London.
20. TRANSPORT AND ROAD RESEARCH LABORATORY. The CHART system of assessing structural maintenance needs of highways, Report 153 UC, HMSO, London, 1975.
21. SENIOR, G. M. Highway maintenance—A package of information, Proc. of PTRC Summer Annual Meeting, 1977, PTRC (ERS), London.
22. TECHWEST. Guide to interpretation of Phololog film and systems specifications, Techwest Enterprises Ltd., Vancouver, Canada, 1977.
23. Permanent International Association of Road Congresses Report of the Proceedings, 239–42, XVth World Road Congress, Mexico, 1975, The British National Committee, London.
24. ORGANISATION OF ECONOMIC CO-OPERATION AND DEVELOPMENT. *Road strengthening*, Ch. V-V.6.3, OECD, Paris, 1976.
25. HATHERLEY, L. W. Scrim and its role in maintenance planning, PTRC Highway Maintenance Course, PTRC (ERS), London, 1976.
26. DEPARTMENT OF THE ENVIRONMENT. COBA Manual, DoE, London.
27. HAAS, R. C. G. and KARAN, M. A. A user delay cost model for highway rehabilitation, Transportation Research Board Annual General Meeting 1975, Transportation Research Board, Washington DC.
28. TRANSPORT AND ROAD RESEARCH LABORATORY. Cost of road accidents in Great Britain, Report LR 79, HMSO, London, 1967.
29. TRANSPORT AND ROAD RESEARCH LABORATORY. Pavement deflection measurements and their application to structural maintenance and overlay design, Report LR 571, HMSO, London, 1973.
30. TRANSPORT AND ROAD RESEARCH LABORATORY. A guide to the structural design of pavements for new roads, Road Note 29, 3rd ed., HMSO, London, 1970.
31. PEATTIE, K. R. *J. Inst. Hwy Engrs*, Traffic loading and its influence on the design of flexible pavements and overlays, Dec., 1974.
32. HILL, J. and THORPE, M. R. *J. Inst. Hwy Engrs*, The Deflectograph—a practical concept, Feb., 1976.
33. TRANSPORT AND ROAD RESEARCH LABORATORY. A portable wheel-weighing unit and data recorder, Report LR 391, HMSO, London, 1971.

34. TARA Working Group, County Surveyors' Society, TARA User Manual, The Engineer's Department, Devon County Council.
35. DEPARTMENT OF THE ENVIRONMENT. Deflection measurements and their application to structural maintenance and overlay design for flexible pavements, Technical Memorandum H10/76, DoE, London, 1976.
36. LISTER, N. W. and KENNEDY, C. K. A system for the prediction of pavement life and design of pavement strengthening, Proc. 4th Int. Conf. on the Struct. Design of Asphalt Pavement, 629–48, Ann Arbor, Michigan, 1977.
37. LEES, G. Skid resistance of bituminous and concrete surfacings, Chapter 6, in *Developments in Highway Pavement Engineering—1*, P. S. Pell (ed.), Applied Science Publishers, London, 1978.

Chapter 6

PAVEMENT ENGINEERING IN DEVELOPING COUNTRIES†

OVERSEAS UNIT, TRANSPORT AND ROAD RESEARCH LABORATORY, UK

SUMMARY

This chapter by the Overseas Unit of the Transport and Road Research Laboratory provides the reader with the background and reasons for the differences between pavement engineering in temperate climates and in developing countries with tropical or sub-tropical climates.

The importance of earth and gravel roads in developing countries is emphasised, and commonly used methods of pavement design for bitumen surfaced roads are described and compared. Recent developments in techniques and equipment for improving construction standards and for assessing road performance are described.

The use of appropriate forms of contract is briefly discussed and the need to improve knowledge of the factors which would enable total transport costs to be minimised is emphasised.

INTRODUCTION

Since most developing countries lie in the tropics or sub-tropics the differences between pavement engineering in temperate industrialised countries and developing countries are often thought of almost exclusively in terms of climatic differences. Whilst these differences are substantial, a considerable body of knowledge exists that enables experienced designers

† This chapter by the Overseas Unit of the Transport and Road Research Laboratory is included by permission of the Director of the Laboratory. Crown copyright 1977.

157

to incorporate reasonably satisfactory provisions within their designs for all but the most extreme effects of tropical climates.

Equally important differences between pavement engineering in developing countries and industrialised countries are the greater variability of construction materials, quality of construction, and the larger fluctuations in the volume and weight of road traffic that are typically encountered in developing countries.

Because of the large variability of these factors the design of road pavements in developing countries must either include a higher 'factor of safety' than is usual in industrialised countries, or a higher risk of failure must be accepted. The latter course is the one most commonly adopted. It is an advantage in that it minimises the demands made by roadbuilding on scarce capital resources, and the disadvantages of partial or premature pavement failure are much reduced by the short 'design life' generally adopted and the relative ease with which repairs can be made on the typically uncongested roads.

In the few fortunate oil-rich developing countries the pavement engineering situation has, however, radically changed in recent years. Low risks of failure and long design lives are now often demanded in these countries; designers respond by adopting generous factors of safety to compensate for the large uncertainties that remain in the prediction of traffic and the variability of materials and quality of construction.

TABLE 1

SELECTED STATISTICS OF ROADS AND ROAD TRANSPORT IN DEVELOPING AND INDUSTRIALISED COUNTRIES

Country	Gross national product per capita US $ (ref. 1)	Length of bitumenised or concrete road km × 10^3 (ref. 2)	Length of earth or gravel road km × 10^3 (ref. 2)	Density of road networks km per km^2 (ref. 3)	Numbers of commercial vehicles[a] per km of road
United States	6 670	2 925	3 215	0·66	4·29
France	5 440	707	87	1·4	2·78
United Kingdom	3 590	331	12	1·49	5·36
Brazil	920	77	1 235	0·15	0·76
Sierra Leone	190	1	6	0·10	0·64
India	140	409	486	0·27	0·46
Ethiopia	100	3	6	0·007	1·19

[a] Trucks and buses.

An important aspect of pavement engineering in developing countries that has no parallel in most industrialised countries is the extent to which unsurfaced roads contribute to national road networks. In developing countries unsurfaced roads carrying several hundred vehicles per day are not uncommon, and unsurfaced roads of all types play a vital role in the economic and social life of many of these countries. The techniques of constructing and maintaining unsurfaced roads are thus an important part of pavement engineering in developing countries.

The selected statistics shown in Table 1 illustrate the differences between roads and road transport in developing countries and in industrialised countries.

HIGHWAY PAVEMENT ENGINEERING

Highway pavement engineering may be defined as the process of designing, constructing, and maintaining highway pavements in order to provide a desired 'level of service' for traffic. In the pavement design part of this process, designers make assumptions about the methods of construction that will be employed and the level of maintenance that the pavement will receive throughout its design life. Clearly both the initial standard of construction and the level of maintenance affect the level of service provided by the pavement, these two factors being very closely inter-related. In the USA Hudson[4] has drawn attention to the interdependence of these factors and the fact that the design and construction of a road pavement is not a single-phase process, but is merely the beginning of a continuing process in which maintenance, traffic, climate and the required level of service are all contributory factors. In Britain the costs of constructing and maintaining road pavements over a 50 year design life have been analysed.[5]

In the case of low-cost roads, typical of most developing countries, the influence of maintenance on the level of service provided by the pavement will generally be much stronger than is the case with heavier duty pavements. For unsurfaced roads the level of maintenance is as at least as important as the initial construction standard in determining the level of service provided.

Ideally at the design stage, the designer, in consultation with the authority that will maintain the road, should select the combination of initial construction standard and subsequent maintenance that will provide the level of service required over the design life of the road in the most cost-effective way. In practice, in developing countries the designer rarely has sufficient information to make a quantified assessment of the appropriate balance between the initial construction standard and the level of maintenance, and because of uncertainty about the provision of maintenance when it is needed, he will often tend to enhance the standard of initial construction so as to minimise future maintenance requirements. Some advances are being made however in providing designers with quantitative information on the 'trade-off' between the standards of construction and maintenance of roads typical of those found in developing countries. In recent years models have been produced that allow designers not only to quantify the interaction between construction and maintenance standards, but also to calculate their combined effect on vehicle operating costs, and hence to produce a design and specify a maintenance strategy that will minimise the sum of construction, maintenance, and vehicle operating costs over the design life of the pavement. The sum of these three costs has been called the 'total transportation cost', and whilst these costs do not by any means represent all the costs involved in road transport, they are by far the most significant costs on non-urban roads in developing countries.

Cost Models

The initiative for developing cost models for roads in developing countries was taken in the early 1970s by the World Bank. The World Bank recognised the need to improve knowledge of the interaction between road construction costs, road maintenance costs, and vehicle operating costs, in order to improve the quality of investment decisions in the roads sector in developing countries. As a first step a computer model was built on the basis of existing knowledge.[6] Subsequently a major study was undertaken in East Africa by the Overseas Unit of the UK Transport and Road Research Laboratory (TRRL)[7,8] in collaboration with the World Bank to improve knowledge of the effects of road conditions on vehicle operating costs and the rates of deterioration of road pavements. As a result of these field studies empirical relationships were derived that have been incorporated into a computer model (RTIM).[9] This model calculates the sum of road construction costs, road maintenance costs, and vehicle operating costs over the 'design life' of the road for a non-urban road project in a developing country.

Further improvements to these empirical relationships will be forthcoming from World Bank sponsored studies which are in progress in Brazil[10] and India, and from TRRL studies in the Caribbean. In addition to these field studies, model development is being undertaken by the

Massachusetts Institute of Technology with the objective of producing a model capable of evaluating 'total transport costs' for road networks rather than just for single road links.

EARTH AND GRAVEL ROADS

Not surprisingly the engineering of earth and gravel roads has received much less attention from highway engineers and research workers than the engineering of surfaced roads. Most of the technical literature on unsurfaced roads is concerned with the techniques and the organisation of maintenance, and the selection and specification of natural materials for constructing gravel roads. Several methods have been published for designing the thickness of unsurfaced roads on a structural design basis, and three of these methods are described below. However, the relevance of the concept of structural design to unsurfaced roads is not widely accepted.

In recent years there has been a growing awareness of the need to improve knowledge of the relationships between the construction and maintenance standards, the climate, the traffic, and vehicle operating costs on unsurfaced roads. The need arises because of the desire of transport planners to improve the quality of investment decisions in the rural road sector in developing countries. A considerable amount of unrecorded local knowledge about the interaction between many of these factors exists in developing countries, but quantified data is very scarce.

Earth Roads

The distinction between earth and gravel roads is rarely well-defined, but a commonly accepted distinction is that earth roads are constructed only of the natural materials that are encountered on the road line or immediately adjacent to it. Gravel roads on the other hand may incorporate imported material, normally a selected natural gravelly material, but sometimes processed gravels may be used.

The best service will be obtained from earth roads if they are located on the better drained parts of the terrain, and on the more granular soils if any choice of soil type is available. In most situations skill in locating earth roads in the landscape is thus fundamental to their subsequent performance. Often the location of earth roads is undertaken on the basis of a brief reconaissance of the ground by an engineer, but in complex terrain much better results will be obtained by using terrain evaluation

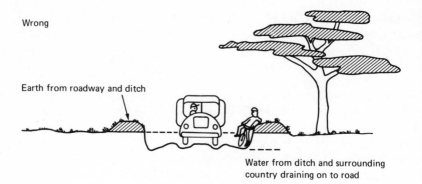

Wrong

Earth from roadway and ditch

Water from ditch and surrounding country draining on to road

Typical sunken road

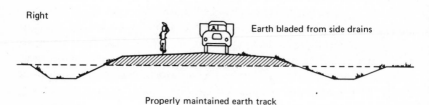

Right

Earth bladed from side drains

Properly maintained earth track

FIG. 1. Correctly and incorrectly maintained earth track.

techniques[11,12] assisted by aerial photography and other remotely sensed ground data.

Clearly the traffic-bearing ability of earth roads depends heavily on the type of soil forming the running surface, and on the prevailing moisture conditions. The ability of earth roads to carry traffic can be substantially enhanced if they are 'engineered' by such measures as raising the formation in low-lying areas, clearing trees and shrubs well back from the road so that the sun and wind can more readily dry out the road surface when it is wet, cambering the surface, and cutting suitable side-drains. The principles of good construction and maintenance practice for earth roads are illustrated in Fig. 1. In favourable circumstances earth roads can carry substantial volumes of traffic, as is evidenced for example by the behaviour of 'sabkha' roads[13] in certain arid areas, and the roads built on the 'red-coffee' soils in Kenya.

A comprehensive guide to the construction and maintenance of earth roads has been written by Mellier.[14] More recently some interesting research on the trafficability of soils has been undertaken at Vicksburg,[15] the results of which are illustrated by the nomograph shown in Fig. 2. This nomograph indicates the number of repetitions of wheel loads of different magnitudes that can be carried by soils of different strengths. The definition of the terminal condition in this work was when the rut-depth in the soil exceeded 75 mm. If the strength of an earth road is known (in terms of its California Bearing Ratio (CBR) value), the nomograph permits predictions to be made of the load carrying ability of the road.

Gravel Roads

There are two basic attitudes to the design of the thickness of gravel roads. One of these is the quantitative structural design approach, examples of which are the methods suggested by Mellier[14] and Hammitt.[16] This approach presents the designer with the difficult problem of deciding what moisture content should be assumed for the subgrade soil and the gravel layer, since clearly in seasonal climates there will be a large change in moisture content and hence the strength of these materials between the wet and dry seasons.

The other approach to the design of gravel roads is that described by O'Reilly and Millard[17] in which the assumption is made that thickness design of gravel roads is unnecessary, and the important issue is the

TABLE 2
PLASTICITY CHARACTERISTICS PREFERRED FOR GRAVEL SURFACINGS[17]

Climate	Liquid limit not to exceed (%)	Plasticity index range (%)	Linear shrinkage range (%)
Moist temperate and wet tropical	35	4–9	2·5–5
Seasonally wet tropical	45	6–20	4–10
Arid or semi-arid	55	15–30	8–15

selection of gravel material with specified grading and plasticity characteristics which is placed in a layer of standard thickness (150 to 200 mm). This approach is the one usually adopted in developing countries in the tropics in which subgrades under adequately maintained gravel roads are commonly strong enough for the greater part of the year to support the imposed wheel loads with no more than 150 mm of gravel cover. Table 2

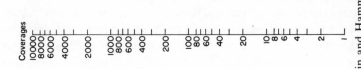

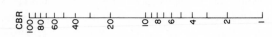

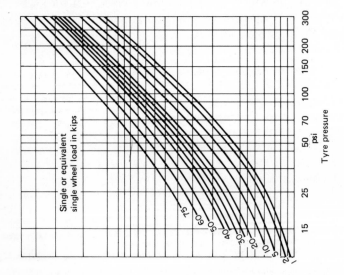

FIG. 2.   Relation between load, repetition, tyre pressure, and CBR for unsurfaced soils. (After Ahlvin and Hammitt[15]).

gives values for the plasticity characteristics of gravel surfacing materials typically specified in different climatic zones. In either case provision has to be made for the replacement of gravel that is lost over a period of time due to the action of traffic and weather.

In practice the choice of gravel material is limited by what is available, and economy in design depends on the skill and resources that can be deployed to locate the very best materials that exist within an economic haul distance from the road. The terrain evaluation approach[11,12] can be of great assistance in the location of gravel materials within the landscape.

In areas with strongly seasonal climates it may not be economically feasible to build gravel roads on plastic subgrades that are capable of sustaining traffic throughout the wet season without excessive deformation. In these circumstances the level of service provided can usually be maintained at an acceptable level by increasing the frequency of grading, or in some areas where this is not possible roads are closed for short periods after heavy and prolonged rain to prevent traffic causing excessive deformation when the subgrade is saturated.

Maintenance has a very strong influence on the performance of gravel roads. At traffic flows of more than 30 or so vehicles per day most gravel roads require grading at regular intervals of time to remove corrugations, to restore the transverse profile, and to bring back into the centre of the road gravel that has been thrown to the sides by the action of traffic. In addition, the clearing of side ditches and the restoration of material removed by erosion are required at regular intervals. All these operations are necessary if the level of service provided by a gravel road is to be maintained, but perhaps the crucial operation is the maintenance of an adequate camber. Camber must be sufficient to prevent rainwater being retained on the surface of the road. If it is not, the road will deteriorate very rapidly in wet weather.

Recent Developments

The techniques of designing and constructing earth and gravel roads have not changed significantly for many years. There are, however, two recent developments that are of some interest. One of these is the growing interest among highway planners and engineers in quantifying, for a particular climatic zone, the relationships between traffic volume, construction standards, rate of deterioration, and maintenance. Knowledge of these relationships is required if cost-effect decisions are to be made about the construction of unsurfaced roads, or economic maintenance strategies are to be devised. In a number of developing countries empirical relationships have been devised in the past that link the frequency of grading necessary to maintain an acceptable level of service to the volume of traffic, and also in some cases to the type of gravel surfacing. Only recently, however, have quantified relationships of this kind been based on systematic measurements of road surface conditions, or included quantification of the effect of surface condition on vehicle operating costs. For example, in the study in East Africa[7,8] relationships linking the following variables were established for several types of gravel road:

(a)   the volume of traffic;
(b)   the longitudinal roughness of the road surface;
(c)   the depth of ruts formed by the traffic;
(d)   the amount of gravel 'lost' from the road surface due to the action of traffic and erosion;
(e)   the longitudinal gradient of the road;
(f)   the rainfall.

Further studies are in progress that will improve these relationships and will extend them to other materials and climatic zones.

A second recent development in the field of earth and gravel road construction is the widespread renewed interest in employing labour-intensive methods of construction in developing countries. In several Asian countries labour-intensive methods have traditionally been employed on a large scale for civil construction projects. In many other developing countries, however, the construction of roads by labour-intensive methods has not hitherto been undertaken except on a small-scale and piecemeal basis. Recent studies sponsored by the World Bank[18] and the International Labour Organisation[19] have shown that labour-intensive methods can in general produce the same quality of construction as equipment-intensive methods, and that they are economically justifiable in countries where the shadow daily wage† for labour is less than about US $1·50 to $2·00. This is the situation in more than forty countries, in several of which national programmes for labour-intensive road construction have recently been started or are planned.

† In many developing countries the wages paid often do not reflect the true value of labour to the economy. It is this latter which is relevant when comparing labour and capital intensive methods and it is termed the 'shadow wage'. For further amplification see 'A guide to project appraisal in developing countries', HMSO, London.

BITUMEN SURFACED ROADS

Current Design Methods

Very few of the various methods of pavement design that are in general use throughout the world have been devised specifically for the design of pavements in tropical developing countries. Two exceptions are the guide issued by the UK TRRL Road Note 31,[20] and the French CEBTP design manual for tropical countries.[21] Other popular methods of pavement design, such as the AASHTO method[22] and its derivatives, though derived empirically in industrialised countries with temperate climates, are nevertheless often used for the design of pavements in the tropics.

Comments on the appropriateness of these methods for designing pavements in tropical developing countries are made below.

TRRL Road Note 31 (Third Edition 1977)

This pavement design guide, issued by the Transport and Road Research Laboratory,[20] gives recommendations for the design of bitumen-surfaced roads carrying up to 2·5 million equivalent standard axles per lane in tropical and sub-tropical countries. The guide offers the designer the choice of two simple standard pavements, and provides for the thickness of the sub-base to be varied to suit the strength of the subgrade.

Particular attention is given in the guide to two aspects of pavement design that are of special importance in most developing countries:

(1) detailed consideration is given to the influence of tropical climates on moisture conditions in road subgrades;

(2) attention is drawn to the advantages of adopting a stage construction approach to road building in situations where traffic growth rates are high or long-term predictions are uncertain.

The guide expresses the strength of the subgrade soil in terms of its CBR measured at a moisture content equal to the wettest moisture condition likely to occur in the subgrade after the road has been constructed.

Traffic loading is expressed in terms of equivalent standard axles, on the same basis as that used in the AASHTO method.[22]

The guide, which has been derived empirically, suffers the disadvantages that all such methods share, namely that it cannot be applied with confidence to design situations that lie outside the range of conditions within which it has been derived. Nevertheless it does offer the designer a wide choice of pavement material options and is suitable for the design of medium and lightly trafficked roads in any tropical or sub-tropical environment.

CEBTP Pavement Design Manual for Tropical Countries (1972)
This pavement design manual[21] is widely used in French-speaking developing countries in the tropics. Traffic is categorised into four classes and a catalogue of four basic pavements is recommended to match these. Subgrade strength is expressed in terms of CBR, and the thickness of the base and sub-base of each class of pavement can be varied within limits to take account of differences in subgrade strength.

The categorisation of the traffic loading can be made in two ways:

(1)   on the basis of the average volume of traffic per day (all vehicles) assuming a design life of 15 years and 30 % 'heavy' vehicles in the traffic stream;

(2)   on the basis of the cumulative number of 'heavy' vehicles passing over the pavement during its design life.

A heavy vehicle is defined as one that has a total weight of more than 3 tonnes.

The guide also suggests that if more than 10 % of axle loads are greater than 13 tonnes extra pavement thickness may be required.

The manual, which is very simple to use, is essentially a modification of the original CBR method of design. It does not attempt to differentiate between axle loads of different magnitudes, and hence it cannot take account of the big differences in damaging power that can exist between similar volumes of traffic in different countries, or even on different roads within the one country.

AASHTO Interim Guide (1972)
This guide,[22] which is based on empirical relationships derived from the AASHO Road Test,[23] was produced primarily for the design of pavements in the USA. Nevertheless it is sometimes used, not always very appropriately, for the design of pavements in developing countries in the tropics.

In the guide the predicted distribution of the axle loads that will traverse the pavement throughout its design life is expressed in terms of the equivalent number of 8·2 tonne 'standard' axles. This is achieved by the application of 'equivalence' factors (see ref. 52). These factors relate the damage done to the pavement by an axle load of any magnitude to the damage done by a standard 8·2 tonne axle load. The factors follow approximately a 'fourth power law'; that is, if an axle load is doubled, the damage it will inflict on the pavement will be sixteen times greater. This concept of axle load equivalence factors is now widely accepted, and is incorporated into several other methods of pavement design. However, there is a great deal of uncertainty about the magnitude of the power in the 'power law', and the extent to which it is influenced by overall pavement strength and the types of materials used in the pavement.

The AASHTO guide defines subgrade strength in terms of a 'soil support value', ranging from one for very weak subgrades, to ten for subgrades as strong as crushed rock base material. Pavement thickness is expressed in terms of a Structural Number (SN), ranging from 1·0 to 6·0, which is an index of the strength of pavement required. This is then modified by the application of a Regional Factor which adjusts the design to suit local climatic conditions. Finally, layer thicknesses are determined, the contribution of the layers of the selected pavement materials to the pavement strength is estimated by applying coefficients (sometimes called 'layer equivalencies') that have been assigned to the commoner materials on the basis of the results of the AASHO test and subsequent experience.

The problem facing a designer applying the AASHTO guide to the design of a pavement in a typical developing country situation is the difficulty in estimating the appropriate Regional Factor to use, and in determining the appropriate coefficients to apply to the pavement materials available. The same problem arises whenever an empirically derived design method is applied in conditions outside the range of experience on which it has been based.

The range of Regional Factors employed in the USA is large, and is rather arbitrarily applied. In dry frost-free regions the Regional Factor used can be as low as 0·5, whilst in regions where subgrades freeze in the winter but thaw out in the spring the Regional Factor used may be as high as 4·0 or 5·0. This range represents an increase in thickness of 50% for pavements with a SN of 2·5 or less, typical of most surfaced roads in developing countries.

In South Africa, where a modified form of the AASHTO design method is employed and the climate ranges from moist sub-tropical to arid, Regional Factors in the range 0·3 to 0·75 are recommended.[24] In Mexico a Regional Factor of 0·2 is used in semi-arid situations.

As regards the appropriate coefficients to apply to different pavement materials, a considerable amount of information exists about the commoner pavement materials used in the USA, such as asphaltic concrete surfacing materials and crushed rock and gravel base materials. In developing countries in the tropics the indigenous pavement materials available will often not have any close parallel in North America and designers using the AASHTO method will have to rely on judgement in assigning coefficients to the materials selected.

Shell Modified Design Charts

The Shell design charts were first published in 1963,[25] but have been modified subsequently to take account of the effects of high road temperatures on the moduli of bituminous materials.[26] They are therefore now better suited to the design of road pavements in developing countries in the tropics. The charts were derived from consideration of the basic properties of bituminous mixes as determined by mechanical tests in the laboratory, and the allowable strains in the subgrade and asphalt surfacing layer. The analytical approach to pavement design, which is the basis of both the original Shell design charts and the more recent more comprehensive method,[26] is fully described in ref. 52.

The original charts are held to have been well-supported by the evidence of the performance of roads, but the recently modified charts have yet to be similarly validated.

In using the modified Shell charts it is necessary to estimate the weighted mean annual air temperature (MAAT) of the location in question. This can be obtained from mean monthly air temperatures by use of a given weighting curve. Simple meteorological information of this kind can usually be obtained in most countries, or can be estimated with adequate accuracy.

Other Methods

Various other methods of pavement design are used from time to time in developing countries. The most significant of these are Road Note 29,[27] the Asphalt Institute method,[28] and the Canadian Good Roads Association method.[29] None of these methods are well suited to the design of roads carrying less than about 500 vehicles a day, which form the majority of the surfaced roads in most developing countries. Moreover, whilst these methods of pavement design can be used to design heavily-trafficked roads in developing countries, they do not have the facility for adjusting designs to take account of different climatic environments.

Comparison of Pavement Design Methods

Valid comparisons between the different methods of pavement design described above are difficult to make. If common factors of safety and criteria for pavement failure were shared by all the methods, a comparison on the basis of the recommended thicknesses of similar materials would be a measure of the relative 'efficiency' or design economy of the different methods.

In fact, the failure criteria and factors of safety inherent in the various methods are all different, and in several methods they are not even clearly defined. Nevertheless some measure of the relative efficiency of the different design methods can be gained by comparing the pavement thicknesses recommended by the various methods for similar levels of traffic loading and subgrade strength.

In order to make these comparisons it is helpful to express pavement thicknesses in terms of a 'structural number', similar in concept to the SN used in the AASHTO design method. In the AASHTO method SN is given by:

$$SN = a_1 D_1 + a_2 D_2 + a_3 D_3$$

where a_1, a_2, and a_3 are layer coefficients, and D_1, D_2, D_3 are layer thicknesses in inches. It should be recognised that assigning coefficients to particular materials can only be a very rough guide to the relative contribution different materials can make to the structural strength of a pavement. It is well known that the effective coefficient of a pavement layer is not only a function of the type of material but is also dependent on the thickness of the layer, the position of the layer in the pavement, the moduli and thicknesses of the other layers, the subgrade characteristics, and other factors. There are thus many reservations about the concept of layer coefficients, but nevertheless it will suffice for the purpose of making a rough comparison between current methods of pavement design.

Because the service temperatures of bituminous surfacings in most developing countries in the tropics are much higher than those experienced in the AASHO Road Test, it is necessary to assume different layer coefficients for bituminous layers from those given in the AASHTO guide if even rough comparisons between different design methods are to be made in the context of tropical environments. The AASHTO guide suggests a coefficient of between 0·44 and 0·40 for asphaltic concrete surfacings, but in a typical developing country situation it is assumed for the purposes of this comparison that 0·20 would be more appropriate. This assumption is made on the basis of the temperature/stiffness relationship for bituminous mixtures implicit in the modified Shell design charts,[26] from which can be deduced the relations shown in Fig. 3 between MAAT and layer coefficient. From Fig. 3 it can be seen that in tropical climates the

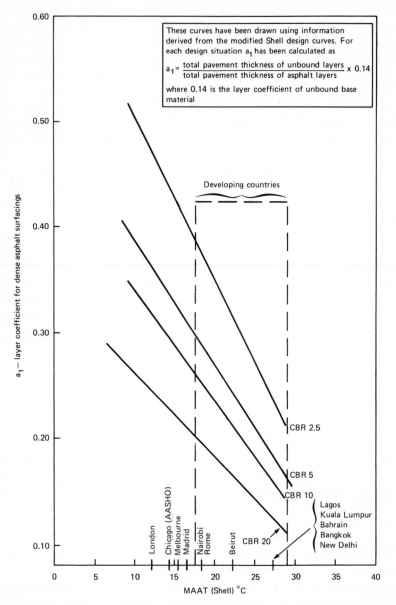

FIG. 3.   Possible variations in surface layer coefficients for differing conditions.

effective layer coefficient for asphalt surfacings ranged from about 0·10 for CBR 20 subgrades in the hottest climates, to about 0·37 for CBR 2·5 subgrades in sub-tropical climates.

Using values of 0·2 for a_1, and the same values for a_2 and a_3 as are given in the AASHTO guide (e.g. granular base $a_2 = 0·14$, sub-base $a_3 = 0·11$), the modified structural numbers implied by the different design recommendations are compared in Fig. 4. For convenience the modified structural number is plotted as 'Tropical Structural Number' (TSN), and Fig. 4 shows how this is related to traffic loading on an average subgrade of CBR 8.

In calculating the TSN values that are plotted in Fig. 4 it was assumed that the pavements had the minimum thickness of bituminous surfacing permitted by each design method. This minimises the influence on TSN of the value adopted for the coefficient a_1, and is typical of developing country pavements which rarely have thick bituminous surfacings.

It is also assumed in Fig. 4 that the subgrade strengths are assessed in the same way for each of the design methods. In fact each method suggests different ways of estimating the appropriate subgrade moisture content and density at which to assess the subgrade strength. These variations increase even further the differences between the designs produced by the different methods shown in Fig. 4.

Similarly, each design method suggests rather different ways of expressing traffic loading. Most methods convert the predicted axle load distributions into an equivalent number of standard axles, but there are considerable differences in the factors used for this.

Accepting these reservations about the basis of this comparison, it can nevertheless be concluded that there are very large differences between the designs produced by the various methods of pavement design, even when the same assumptions of subgrade strength and traffic loading are made. The TSN is in effect an index of pavement thickness, and it can be seen from Fig. 4 that the more conservative design methods recommend pavements almost twice as thick as the least conservative. It can also be seen that the methods of pavement design issued specifically for use in tropical developing countries produce the most economical designs. This partly reflects the different standards of serviceability and failure criteria that are inherent in the different methods, but it also reflects different modes of failure and the absence of the damaging effect of frost in the tropics.

The comparisons made in Fig. 4 demonstrate the degree of uncertainty that exists about the design of more heavily trafficked road pavements in the tropics, and points to the need for more research in this field.

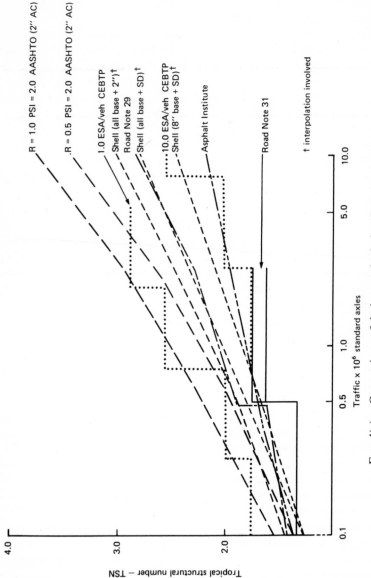

FIG. 4(a).   Comparison of design methods for CBR 8 subgrade.

Notes

— — — — —	R = 1.0 PSI = 2.0 AASHTO (2″ AC)	AASHTO method with R = 1.0 and PSI = 2.0 for a pavement with 2 inches (50mm) of asphaltic concrete (a_1 = 0.44) and using UTAH correlation between S and CBR
— — — — —	R = 0.5 PSI = 2.0 AASHTO (2″ AC)	AASHTO method as above but with regional factor R = 0.5
-------------	Shell (all base + SD)	Shell modified design method assuming surface dressing on a crushed rock base (take $a_1 D_1$ = 0.05). All unbound materials are assumed to be of base quality
-------------	Shell (8″ base + SD)	Shell method as above but assuming surface dressing + 8 inches (200 mm) crushed rock base + sub-base to make up total thickness of unbound material
-----------	Shell (all base + 2″)	Shell modified design method assuming 2 inches of dense asphalt on a crushed rock base. All unbound materials are assumed to be of base quality.
—·—·—·—	Road Note 29	Road Note 29. TRRL method for U.K.
—··——·—·	Asphalt Institute	Asphalt Institute design method assuming quoted minimum thickness of surfacing asphaltic concrete, 6 inches (150 mm) of crushed rock base if necessary and the balance of sub-base material if required
———————	Road Note 31	Road Note 31. TRRL method for developing countries
················	1.0 ESA/veh CEBTP	CEBTP method for tropical developing countries assuming that traffic is equivalent to 1.0 standard axle per commercial vehicle
················	10.0 ESA/veh CEBTP	CEBTP method as above for traffic equivalent to 10 standard axles per commercial vehicle

FIG. 4(b).   Comparison of design methods.

Recent Developments
Axle Loads
In all countries increases in the volume of traffic and the size and weight of
vehicles over the last two or three decades have necessitated the building of
much stronger road pavements than those that sufficed earlier. In
developing countries the rate of growth of traffic loading has been most
dramatic. In part this is a reflection of the relatively small number of
commercial vehicles that were in use in Third World countries twenty years
ago, but it also reflects the absence of effective control of the weights and
axle loads of vehicles in many countries. Indeed in some countries there is
no restriction at all on axle loads.

As a result of the high rate of growth of traffic loading in developing
countries, it is not uncommon for roads to fail prematurely because the

traffic loading in service is several times greater than was assumed in the design. In recent years a considerable amount of information has become available about the axle loads on the roads in a number of developing countries.[30,31] This has shown the strong influence that a relatively small number of vehicles with high axle loads can have on the rate of pavement damage of a typical main road in a developing country. For example, it is possible to envisage a situation in which the regular use of as few as one or two hundred vehicles with 20 tonne axle loads could severely damage a significant proportion of the paved road network of a developing country within a few months. This is because when overall volumes of traffic are low and axle loads are modest, the introduction into the traffic stream of a small proportion of vehicles with 20 tonne axle loads can double or treble the damaging power of the traffic. It is thus very important to control the upper limit of axle loads in developing countries.

This conclusion arises directly from the assumption that an axle load of 20 tonnes is roughly 300 times as damaging as one of 5 tonnes. This is the ratio given by axle load equivalence factors derived from the AASHO Road Test that are used in most methods of pavement design in current use. However, there are considerable doubts about the validity of the AASHO Road Test equivalence factors for use in developing countries. They may under-estimate or over-estimate the damaging effect of heavy axle loads. The main reasons for these doubts are:

(1)   The maximum axle loads used in the AASHO Road Test were 13·6 tonnes for single axles, and 21·8 tonnes for tandem axle sets. In developing countries, single axle loads in excess of 20 tonnes are not uncommon, hence it is necessary to extrapolate well beyond the AASHO test results to derive equivalence factors for these loads.

(2)   There are considerable differences between the various interpretations that have been made of the AASHO Road Test results. Whilst Liddle's analysis[32] is most widely used, the analysis made by Shook and Finn[33] is also used to a considerable extent and these two interpretations give quite different results for the damaging effect of very heavy axle loads.

(3)   Frost was a critical factor in the deterioration of the AASHO Road Test pavements, but it is a negligible factor in most developing countries. In the interpretation of the results an attempt was made to separate the effects of frost on pavement deterioration from the traffic-induced effects, but this was not wholly successful.

(4)   The Road Test pavements were constructed on a weak subgrade,

whereas most pavements in developing countries are built on strong subgrades.

Clearly there is a need to reduce the uncertainty that exists about the damaging power of heavy axle loads in typical developing country situations. Eventually the analytical pavement design approach will be developed to the point where consideration of empirically derived axle load equivalence factors will become irrelevant. However, this goal is still some way off, and in the shorter term research such as that being undertaken in South Africa using heavy vehicle simulators[34] offers the best chance of providing practical answers to these and other pavement design problems.

In recent years the world-wide growth in the movement of freight by road, and the production of a new generation of larger and more powerful commercial vehicles, has prompted governments in many countries to re-examine the maximum axle loads permitted on their national road networks. In general, the larger the vehicle and the heavier the axle load, the cheaper is the tonne–kilometre operating cost. In both developing countries[35] and industrialised countries[36] attempts have been made to deduce the optimum axle load at which the combined cost of vehicle operation, road construction, and road maintenance is minimised. Figure 5 indicates the nature of the relationships between axle load and the tonne–kilometre costs of vehicle operation and road construction and maintenance. There are of course big differences between the ideal 'optimum' axle load, the legal axle load limit, and the range of axle loads that are actually applied to a road system. The influence of the legal axle load limit on the actual distribution of axle loads naturally varies from country to country, depending on the degree of enforcement and other factors. Clearly this aspect must be carefully considered when making an analysis of the merits of a particular legal axle load limit. Similarly if an increase in a legal axle load limit is being considered careful thought must be given to the effects on existing bridge structures and roads; it may well be that the costs of strengthening structures and adding expensive overlays to existing roads outweigh the benefits that would accrue from reduced tonne–kilometre operating costs.

Nevertheless, studies in some countries, notably Australia,[37] have concluded that raising axle load limits would bring substantial national economic benefits. It is probable that similar conclusions could be reached in several developing countries, and that in the future legal axle load limits in the Third World will tend to rise, but that in parallel there will be stricter enforcement of these limits.

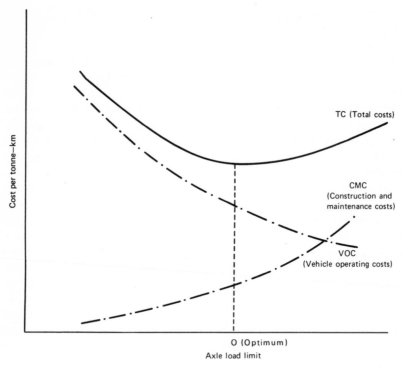

FIG. 5.   The nature of the relation between tonne–kilometre costs and axle load.

Heavy Vehicle Simulator

An important development in the field of pavement engineering in recent years has been the building of four Heavy Vehicle Simulators (HVS) in South Africa.[34] Whilst the contribution these machines are likely to make to the advance of pavement design is of world-wide interest, the fact that they will be used, initially at least, in the sub-tropical climate of South Africa, will be of special interest to those concerned with improving pavement design in developing countries in the tropics.

   Repeated loading tests of pavement materials at laboratory scale as described by Brown[53] has an important part to play in the development of a dependable analytical method of pavement design. However, many research workers believe that the essential validation by full-scale experience of theoretical models based on laboratory experiments can be greatly assisted by the use of intermediate forms of testing of the 'road machine' type. Indeed some research workers believe that without this intermediate step very little further progress can be made towards a reliable mechanistic method of design.

The great asset of 'road machines' is that they apply the load to test pavements through a rolling wheel, and hence they induce the same sort of changes in the directions and magnitudes of the stresses experienced by all elements of the pavement as are experienced in normal service. Several different types of road machine have been used for pavement design research in the past, but the HVS is the first full-scale machine that can be moved easily from place to place and can be used to load *in situ* both ordinarily-constructed roads as well as specially-built full-scale experimental roads and pilot scale pavements.

The HVS can apply a load of up to 100 kN through a dual or single wheel assembly which is traversed over the pavement for a distance of 8 m at a speed of up to 14 km h^{-1}. The wheel assembly reciprocates in a heavy steel frame and can apply up to 1400 repetitions of load per hour to the pavement under test. It is thus possible to apply half a million repetitions of load to a pavement in 20 to 30 days.

The prototype HVS has been in use for some time and some limited but useful results have been obtained. It has been used to verify a model that predicts the initiation of traffic-induced cracking in cement-treated roadbases. The HVS proved to be successful for this purpose and it enabled load equivalence factors for a limited number of examples of this type of pavement to be studied.[38] It was found that a 'power law' of 6·0 to 6·7 applies to such pavements, as opposed to the power of 4·0 to 4·5 that has been generally assumed hitherto. This result has considerable significance for pavement engineering in tropical developing countries where cement bound materials are more commonly used for roadbases than in most industrialised countries.

With three more HVS machines coming into service in 1977 a significant increase in the rate of acquisition of knowledge of this kind can be anticipated.

The Design of Bituminous Surfacings for High Service Temperatures
The large increase in recent years of the length of road in tropical developing countries that requires a premixed bituminous surfacing has focused the attention of highway engineers on the need to improve the design of surfacings for tropical conditions. For many years bituminous surfacings of the asphaltic concrete type have been widely used in hot climates, and the mix design procedures for achieving high stability mixes are well-established. Experience has shown, however, that such mixes,

whilst having a high resistance to deformation, are prone to cracking and are difficult to compact. It is now recognised that even for high temperature service conditions high stability is not all-important, and that more attention should be given in designing mixes to the properties of flexibility, durability and workability. The high stability of asphaltic concrete is mainly dependent on aggregate interlock and inter-particle friction which are enhanced by the careful proportioning of coarse and fine aggregates to produce a continuously graded mixture.

In Britain, with its temperate climate, such mixes have never been popular and virtually all heavy-duty bituminous wearing courses are composed of a gap-graded type of mix known as hot rolled asphalt. In effect this is a stone-filled sand asphalt in which the stiffness of the sand–filler–binder mortar provides the overall stability of the mix. Whilst such mixes are more prone to deformation than continuously graded mixes, they are more tolerant of variations in mix composition, more flexible, and easier to compact. At British temperatures gap-graded mixes have proved to be very satisfactory, and interest is growing in the use of such materials for road surfacings in the tropics.[39] It has been found that modified forms of hot-rolled asphalt can be produced with adequate stability to resist deformation at high temperatures without sacrificing the advantages of this type of mix.[26,40] To enhance the stability of these mixes it is desirable to use a stiffer bitumen (60/70 pen, or 40/50 pen if available) than that normally used for asphaltic concrete (80/100 pen). The problems of mix design for both gap-graded rolled asphalt and continuously-graded asphaltic concrete are fully discussed in ref. 54.

For less-heavily trafficked roads in developing countries, which nevertheless require a premix bituminous surfacing, bitumen-macadams are being used successfully. Dense bitumen-macadam is virtually the same as asphaltic-concrete except that it has a rather higher voids content. Open-textured bitumen-macadams, however, have a much higher voids content and are permeable. For situations where impermeability is not required they provide a low-cost mix which is easy to make and lay, and which has a wide tolerance to variations in mix composition. They are thus well suited for overlaying lightly trafficked roads that still retain an impermeable surface but require a levelling or friction course.

In many developing countries the most economic and appropriate surfacing for the majority of paved roads is a single or multiple surface dressing.[41] Unfortunately in many countries the difficulty in achieving adequate control of the surface-dressing process means that the lives of surface dressings are much shorter than they could be. Great difficulty is experienced in maintaining binder distributors so that they can apply an even film of binder at the required rate of spread. Similarly it is very difficult to maintain adequate standards of aggregate size, shape, and cleanliness. Some of the effects of these deficiencies can be minimised by such techniques as the pre-treatment of the chippings with a light coating of tar, creosote or diesel to suppress dust and to aid adhesion. Deficiencies in binder distribution are virtually impossible to counter, though they can be mitigated to some extent by the application of a light 'fog-spray' of binder and a sprinkling of sand or rock dust after the chippings have been spread on the main binder film. This technique has value whether or not the main binder film has been sprayed satisfactorily.

Slurry seals,[42] used either alone or in conjunction with a surface dressing, provide very satisfactory surfacings for medium and lightly trafficked roads in many developing countries.

Overlay design

There is no difference in principle between the process of designing strengthening overlays for roads in developing countries and in industrialised countries,[43] see Chapter 4. There are, however, differences in the appropriate methods to use for assessing residual pavement strength and in the stiffnesses of the pavements being strengthened.

In developing countries Benkelman beams are very appropriate for assessing the residual strength of existing roads. More sophisticated equipment such as the deflectograph can equally well be used, but in many cases the cost of such equipment and the difficulty in servicing and operating it in remote areas, will outweigh the advantages it offers as compared with the use of deflection beams. It has been found that well-trained teams equipped with two deflection beams and a loaded truck can achieve rates of survey adequate for a typical road strengthening programme in a developing country, and survey techniques have been developed for this purpose.[44]

The effect of temperature on the stiffness of bituminous materials needs to be carefully considered when undertaking deflection surveys in the tropics. For example, in Britain it is recommended that deflection measurements are not made when road surface temperatures rise above 30 °C, and all measurements of deflection are corrected to their equivalent value at a standard reference temperature of 20 °C. In many developing countries road surface temperatures rarely, if ever, fall below this temperature in daylight hours, thus it is necessary to establish by investigation the typical local deflection/temperature relationships and to select the appropriate standard reference temperature.

Tentative deflection criteria relating deflection to the subsequent traffic-carrying ability of the pavement have been suggested for typical developing country pavements.[19] Further research is needed to extend and validate these criteria in different conditions. The thickness of overlay required to reduce pavement deflections to the required 'design' level is best established by local experience, but if this is lacking the curves derived from British experience[45] can be used as a guide, suitably modified by judgement to take account of differences in materials and service conditions.[46]

Impact (Square) Rollers

The idea of an impact roller was first considered in the 1930s and five-sided prototype machines were built in the early 1950s. Although these machines were used successfully in the 1960s[47] to compact material in thick layers, the machines were impractical because of the problems created by the widely fluctuating loads at the drawbar. The Council of Scientific and Industrial Research (CSIR) in South Africa[48] have studied and solved these problems and have developed a four-sided 'square' roller of 8000 kg or 10 000 kg weight. Its compactive effort is derived from the energy of the mass falling from the corners to the faces whilst being towed at about $12 \, \text{km h}^{-1}$. This compactive effort is many times greater than that obtained from the static mass of the roller. The roller can be raised free of the ground onto carrier wheels to pass over bridges or culverts which might be damaged by the impact blows.

The main advantage of impact rollers is their ability to compact non-cohesive materials in thick layers and at low moisture contents. A considerable amount of experience has now been gained in the compaction of uniform Kalahari sands with impact rollers. It has been shown that these rollers are very effective in compacting material below 0·5 m and up to depths of 4 m below the surface. The upper 0·5 m may sometimes be loosened by the impact compaction process, and must subsequently be compacted by other machines. In very loose materials compaction may have to be carried out through a blanket layer of more cohesive material.

In a series of tests[48] to compare the effectiveness of impact and vibratory rollers on a uniform marine sand it was suggested that the depth influence for the impact roller was about 3 m compared with 1·8 m for the 4500 kg vibratory roller and 2·2 m for the 9000 kg vibratory roller. It has also been suggested that a 15 000 kg vibratory roller may give a performance comparable to a 10 000 kg impact roller.

The main disadvantage of impact compaction is the surface deformations produced by the roller and the loosening of the top layers in certain materials. For this reason this compaction technique is only suitable for earthworks and subgrade preparation and not for the compaction of pavement layers.

CONCRETE ROADS

Concrete roads are uncommon in developing countries for a variety of reasons. For instance in many countries cement has been in short supply for many years and road construction projects are often long distances from the nearest cement factory. Hence cement, if it is obtainable, is likely to be relatively very expensive by the time it is transported to site. Also in developing countries the construction of roads in stages makes sound economic sense, and concrete construction is not well-suited to stage construction. Furthermore, the advantages of concrete pavements over flexible pavements are most marked on weak subgrades, whilst in general, subgrades in tropical developing countries are relatively strong.

For these and other reasons very few concrete roads have been built in developing countries. On the other hand, the rapid rise in the price of bitumen in recent years may prompt a renewed interest in concrete road construction in those countries that have adequate supplies of cement. It is also possible that more concrete roads may be built if they prove to be well-suited to labour intensive methods of construction, as seems possible.

ASSESSING RISKS

Decision Making

Formal decision analysis is not widely used in highway engineering, nor indeed in civil engineering as a whole. This may be because in most civil construction much emphasis is placed on design against failure, rather than on design for the optimum use of available resources. This attitude is perfectly legitimate in cases where the failure of a structure would be catastrophic, such as the failure of a dam or a major bridge. There are other types of civil engineering construction, however, in which 'failure', if it occurs, is not catastrophic, and the costs of accepting different levels of risk of failure can be quantified and should be inherent in the design process. Highway pavements are in this category since pavement 'failures' rarely have disastrous economic or social consequences, and seldom result in a road becoming completely unusable by vehicles. Indeed even the definition of the 'failure' of a road pavement is very arbitrary, and is usually expressed in terms of a certain degree of cracking or surface deformation. Formal decision analysis, which provides a means of balancing technical and financial risks, should therefore be part of the pavement design process. In the process it may be necessary to make subjective as well as quantitative assessments of uncertainties,[49] but this is much better than ignoring entirely the lack of precision that is inherent in pavement engineering, and it is likely to result in a more efficient use of the available resources.

Improved Forms of Contract

In most developing countries road construction is undertaken both by direct labour and by contract. The proportion of the total that is carried out by contract varies considerably from country to country, depending on the size and efficiency of the direct labour organisation and the magnitude of the national road construction and maintenance programme.

The traditional forms of contract used in industrialised countries are often inappropriate for road construction projects in developing countries, where the degree of uncertainty about many aspects of a project may be high. High risks mean high contract prices, and clearly it is in the clients' interest to apply a system of contract that can operate efficiently and fairly in a situation of uncertainty without incurring excessive costs. Recent research[50] that has been undertaken on appropriate forms of contract for use in conditions of uncertainty is particularly relevant to road construction in developing countries. This research indicates that an adaptation of the target price form of contract is likely to be most suitable. Target price contracts are essentially cost-plus contracts with specific incentives built into them to encourage all parties to reduce costs. The form of contract tends to compel the client to make a detailed appraisal of the true objectives of a project and the risks likely to be encountered in its execution. Such an approach is likely to focus the client's attention on policy issues such as the appropriateness of specifications and the use of low-grade materials.

FUTURE NEEDS

There is an urgent need to improve knowledge of the many factors that influence the cost of transport on earth and gravel roads in developing countries. Better knowledge is required of the interaction between vehicles and the roads on which they run, with a view to balancing both vehicle design and road design so as to minimise total transport costs. Improved quantification of the rates of deterioration of earth and gravel roads is necessary in order to assess maintenance needs in economic terms, and to plan cost-effective maintenance strategies. In quantifying the rates of deterioration of unsurfaced roads it will be necessary to separate the effects of traffic and climate, and to define better those surface characteristics of unpaved roads that have the greatest influence on vehicle operating costs. The influence on total transport costs of the method of construction of roads, whether plant-intensive, intermediate, or labour-intensive, also merits investigation.

In the field of paved roads the development of an improved method of pavement design appropriate to developing countries in the tropics is certainly needed. Initially the extension of the existing methods will no doubt be undertaken, assisted by laboratory-scale studies of pavement materials and full-scale pavement studies using accelerated loading devices such as the heavy vehicle simulator. In the longer term, however, a universal analytical method of pavement design is required, sufficiently well calibrated to enable it to accommodate the wide range of environmental conditions and materials that are encountered in developing countries.[51]

The interaction between initial construction standards and subsequent maintenance merits further attention, as does the extent to which maintenance can counter pavement deterioration. There is also a need to develop appropriate specifications for locally-occurring road-building materials, many of which may not meet existing specifications, but are nevertheless quite capable of providing satisfactory service.

In conclusion, it is necesssary for pavement engineers in developing countries to think more in terms of the design, construction, and maintenance of road pavements as being parts of a system, all parts of which interact with each other and with the vehicles that use the roads. The function of the pavement engineer is to manage this system in such a way that the service the system supplies to the community over a period of time is as cost-effective as possible.

REFERENCES

1. WORLD BANK. *World Bank Atlas*, 11th ed., World Bank, Washington DC, 1976.
2. INTERNATIONAL ROAD FEDERATION. Road and motor vehicle statistics for 1975, International Road Federation, Geneva, 1976.
3. UNITED NATIONS. *Statistical year book* 1975, 27th ed., United Nations, New, York, 1976.

4. HUDSON, W. R. State of the art in predicting pavement reliability from input variability, Contract Report 5-75-7, US Army Engineer, Waterways Experiment Station, Vicksburg, 1975.

5. ROAD RESEARCH LABORATORY. The costs of constructing and maintaining flexible and concrete pavements over 50 years, RRL Report LR 256, Ministry of Transport, Crowthorne, 1969.

6. MOAVENZADEH, F. Investment strategies for developing areas: analytical model for choices of strategies in highway transportation, Department of Civil Engineering Research Report No. 72-62, Cambridge, Mass. (Mass. Inst. of Tech.), 1972.

7. HODGES, J. W., ROLT, J. and JONES, T. E. The Kenya road transport cost study: research on road deterioration, TRRL Report LR 673, Department of the Environment, Transport and Road Research Laboratory, Crowthorne, 1975.

8. HIDE, H., ABAYNAYAKA, S. W., SAYER, I. and WYATT, R. J. The Kenya road transport cost study: research on vehicle operating costs, TRRL Report LR 672, Department of the Environment, Transport and Road Research Laboratory, Crowthorne, 1975.

9. ROBINSON, R., HIDE, H., HODGES, J. W., ABAYNAYAKA, S. W. and ROLT, J. A road transport investment model for developing countries, TRRL Report LR 674, Department of the Environment, Transport and Road Research Laboratory, Crowthorne, 1975.

10. REPUBLIC FEDERATIVA DO BRASIL. Research on the inter-relationship between costs of highway construction, maintenance and utilization. Inception Report, Empresa Bresileira de Planejamento de Transportes (CEIPOT), Brasilia, 1976.

11. BEAVEN, P. J. and LAWRANCE, C. J. The application of terrain evaluation to road engineering, Proceedings of the Conference on Road Engineering in Asia and Australasia, Kuala Lumpur 11–16 June 1973, sponsored by the Institution of Engineers, Malaysia and The Public Works Department, West Malaysia, Kuala Lumpur (Institution of Engineers), p. 7, 1973.

12. DOWLING, J. W. F. and WILLIAMS, F. H. P. The use of aerial photographs in materials surveys and classification of landforms (Paper No. 9), Conference on Civil Engineering Problems Overseas, London (Institute of Civil Engineers), pp. 209–36, 1964.

13. ELLIS, C. I. and RUSSELL, R. B. C. The use of salt-laden soils (sabkha) for low cost roads, Proceedings of Conference on Low Cost Roads, Kuwait 25–28 November, Arab Engineers Federation and Kuwait Society of Engineers (TRRL Ref. PA 78/74), 1974.

14. MELLIER, G. *La route en terre*, Editions Eyrolles, Paris, 1968.

15. AHLVIN, R. G. and HAMMITT II, G. M. Load supporting capability of low volume roads, Proceedings of Workshop on Low Volume Roads, Boise, Idaho, Transportation Research Board, Special Report No. 160, Washington, 1976.

16. HAMMITT II, G. M. Thickness requirements for unsurfaced roads and airfields, bare base support, Project 3782-65, Technical Report S-70-5, US Army Engineer Waterways Experiment Station, Vicksburg, Mississippi, July 1970.

17. O'REILLY, M. P. and MILLARD, R. S. Roadmaking materials and pavement design in tropical and sub-tropical countries, RRL Report LR 279, Ministry of Transport, Transport and Road Research Laboratory, Crowthorne, 1969.

18. HARRAL, C. G., SUD, I. K. and COUKIS, B. P. Scope for the substitution of labour and equipment in civil construction, World Conference on Transport Research: Transport Decisions in an Age of Uncertainty, Rotterdam, 1977.

19. ALLAL, M. and EDMONDS, G. A. Manual on the planning of labour-intensive road construction, International Labour Office, Geneva, 1977.

20. TRANSPORT AND ROAD RESEARCH LABORATORY. A guide to the structural design of bitumen surfaced roads in tropical and sub-tropical countries, Road Note No. 31, 3rd ed., Department of the Environment, Department of Transport, HMSO, London, 1977.

21. CENTRE EXPERIMENTAL DE RECHERCHES ET D'ETUDES DU BÂTIMENT ET DES TRAVAUX PUBLICS, Manuel de dimensionnement de chaussees pour les pays tropicaux Secretariat d'Etat aux Affaires Etrangeres, Paris, October 1972.

22. AMERICAN ASSOCIATION OF STATE HIGHWAY AND TRANSPORTATION OFFICIALS. AASHTO interim guide for design of pavement structures 1972, Washington DC, 1974.

23. HIGHWAY RESEARCH BOARD. The AASHO Road Test, Report 7, Summary Report Highway Research Board Special Report No. 61G, Washington DC (National Research Council), 1962.

24. COUNCIL FOR SCIENTIFIC AND INDUSTRIAL RESEARCH. Asphalt pavement design for national roads 1970, National Institute for Road Research Technical Recommendation for Highways TRH 4, Pretoria, 1971.

25. SHELL INTERNATIONAL PETROLEUM COMPANY. *Shell 1963 design charts for flexible pavements*, Shell International Petroleum Co., London, 1963.

26. CLAESSEN, A. I. M., EDWARDS, J. M., SOMMER, P. and UGE, P. Asphalt paving design, the Shell method, Proc. 4th Int. Conf. on the Struct. Design of Asphalt Pavements, 1977, Univ. of Michigan, Ann Arbor, pp. 39–74.

27. ROAD RESEARCH LABORATORY. A guide to the structural design of pavements for new roads, Road Note No. 29, 3rd ed., Department of the Environment, HMSO, London, 1970.

28. ASPHALT INSTITUTE. Thickness design—full depth asphalt pavement structures for highways and streets, Manual Series No. 1, Rev. Eighth ed., August 1970.

29. CANADIAN GOOD ROADS ASSOCIATION. A guide to the structural design of flexible and rigid pavements in Canada, CGRA, 1965.

30. ELLIS, C. I. and POTOCKI, F. P. Axle load distribution on roads overseas, Abu Dhabi and Qatar, 1970–71, TRRL Report LR572, Department of the Environment, Transport and Road Research Laboratory, Crowthorne, 1973.

31. JONES, T. E. Axle loads on paved roads in Kenya, TRRL Report LR 763, Department of the Environment, Department of Transport, Transport and Road Research Laboratory, Crowthorne, 1977.

32. LIDDLE, W. J. Application of AASHO Road Test results to the design of flexible pavement structures, 1st Int. Conf. on the Struct. Design of Asphalt Pavements, Univ. of Michigan, 20–24 August 1962, Ann Arbor, 1962.

33. SHOOK, J. F. and FINN, F. N. Thickness design relationships for asphalt pavements. Proc. of the Int. Conf. on the Struct. Design of Asphalt Pavements, Univ. of Michigan, Ann Arbor, 1962.

34. RICHARDS, R. G., PATERSON, W. D. O. and LOESCH, M. D. The NITRR heavy vehicle simulator: description and operational logistics, Technical Report RP/9/77, National Institute for Transport and Road Research, Pretoria, 1977.

35. ETHIOPIAN ROAD AUTHORITY. The economics of selecting appropriate legal axle load limits, Conference on Highway, Maintenance and Rehabilitation, Ghana 22–29 November 1977, United Nations Economic Commission for Africa.

36. BRINCK, C. E. Optimalt axeltryck (Optimum axle loads), Statens Vaginstitut Meddelande 92 Stockholm, 1966.

37. NATIONAL ASSOCIATION OF AUSTRALIAN STATE ROAD AUTHORITIES. A study of the economics of road vehicle limits—features, recommendations and implementation, 8th Australian Road Research Board Conference, Perth, August 1976.

38. PATERSON, W. D. O. An evaluation of the heavy vehicle simulator as a tool for measuring pavement behaviour, Technical Report RP/5/76, National Institute for Transport and Road Research, Pretoria, 1977.

39. MARAIS, C. P. Gap-graded Asphalt Surfacings: the S. African Scene, Proc. 2nd Conf. on Asphalt Pavements for Southern Africa, Durban, 1974.

40. GROTH, P. J. Overlay design in Natal, Proc. 1st Conf. on Asphalt Pavements for Southern Africa, Durban, 1969.

41. NATIONAL ASSOCIATION OF AUSTRALIAN STATE ROAD AUTHORITIES. Principles and practice of bituminous surfacings, Vol. 1, Sprayed work, National Association of Australian State Road Authorities, Sydney, 1975.

42. NATIONAL INSTITUTE FOR ROAD RESEARCH. Technical recommendations for highways TRH 3, bituminous surface treatments for newly constructed rural roads, National Institute for Road Research, Pretoria, 1971.

43. ELLIS, C. I. and LIAUTAUD, G. The design and construction of strengthening overlays for roads, Paper B, Conference on Highway Engineering in Africa, Addis Ababa, April 1974, United Nations Economic Commission for Africa.

44. SMITH, H. R. A deflection survey technique for pavement evaluation in developing countries, TRRL Report LR 525, Department of the Environment, Transport and Road Research Laboratory, Crowthorne, 1973.

45. LISTER, N. W. and KENNEDY, C. K. A system for the prediction of pavement life and design of pavement strengthening, Proc. 4th Int. Conf. on the Struct. Design of Asphalt Pavements, Univ. of Michigan, Ann Arbor, 1977.

46. BULMAN, J. N. and SMITH, H. R. Pavement performance and deflection studies on Malaysian roads, TRRL Report LR 795, Department of the Environment, Department of Transport, Transport and Road Research Laboratory, Crowthorne, 1977.

47. CLEGG, B. and BERRANGE, A. R. Civil Engineer in South Africa, **13**(3), 1971.

48. CLIFFORD, J. M. Impact rolling and construction techniques, 8th Australian Road Research Board Conference, Perth, August 1976.

49. ELLIS, C. I. Risk and the pavement design decision in developing countries, TRRL Report LR 667, Department of the Environment, Transport and Road Research Laboratory, Crowthorne, 1975.

50. PERRY, J. G. and THOMPSON, P. A. Target and cost-reimbursable construction contracts—a study of their use and implications, Construction Industry Research and Information Association, Report No. 56, London, 1975.

51. CRONEY, D. and BULMAN, J. N. The influence of climatic factors on the structural design of flexible pavements, Proc. 3rd Int. Conf. on the Struct. Design of Asphalt Pavements, London 11–15 September 1972, Vol. 1, Univ. of Michigan, Ann Arbor, 1972.

52. PEATTIE, K. R. Flexible pavement design, Chapter 1, in *Developments in Highway Pavement Engineering*—1, P. S. Pell (ed.), Applied Science Publishers, London, 1978.

53. BROWN, S. F. Material characteristics for analytical pavement design, Chapter 2, in *Developments in Highway Pavement Engineering*—1, P. S. Pell (ed.), Applied Science Publishers, London, 1978.

54. BRIEN, D. Asphalt mix design, Chapter 3, in *Developments in Highway Pavement Engineering*—1, P. S. Pell (ed.), Applied Science Publishers, London, 1978.

INDEX

AASHO Road Test, 168, 171, 176
AASHO slope profilometer, 127
AASHTO design method, 167, 171
AASHTO interim guide, 168
Accident records, 139
Additives, 71
Adsorbed water model, 48
Aggregate suction characteristics, 66
Aggregates, 33–41
  dry density, 36
  grading, 34, 37
  granular sub-base Type 1, 34–6
  granular sub-base Type 2, 36
  moisture content, 35–6
  waste materials, 38–40
Air intrusion value, 50
Asphalt, modulus and layer thickness, 109
Axle loads, 175–6

Bearing capacity, 29
Benkelman beam, 105, 181
Berggren formula, 52
Bitumen surfaced roads in developing countries, 167–83
  high service temperatures, 179–81
  recent developments, 175–83
Bituminous materials, effect of temperature on stiffness of, 181

California Bearing Ratio (CBR) value, 26, 29, 36, 97, 163, 168
Capillary model of frost heave, 45–9, 54
CEBTP design manual, 167, 168
Chalk construction, 15–17
CHART system, 130, 143, 145
Chilled tank unit, 61
China clay sand, 40
CHLOE profilometer, 127
Colliery shales, 18, 38, 71
Compaction
  chalk fills, of, 17
  embankments, of, 10
  plant, 4
Computer, 160
Concrete roads in developing countries, 183
Consolidation, 22
  settlement, 13
Contract, forms of, 184
Cost models in developing countries, 160
Cracking
  cemented roadbase, in, 98
  pavements, of, 95
CRREL test, 56
Cut/fill operation, 3
Cut slope
  failures, 5
  stability, 5–6